NATIONAL NUCLEAR ENERGY SERIES

Manhattan Project Technical Section

Division V — Volume 2

IONIZATION CHAMBERS AND COUNTERS

Experimental Techniques

IONIZATION CHAMBERS AND COUNTERS

Experimental Techniques

by

BRUNO B. ROSSI

Professor of Physics, Massachusetts Institute of Technology

and

HANS H. STAUB

Professor of Physics, Stanford University

First Edition

New York · Toronto · London

McGRAW-HILL BOOK COMPANY, INC.

1949

IONIZATION CHAMBERS AND COUNTERS

Experimental Techniques

Lithoprinted
by
Edwards Brothers, Incorporated
Ann Arbor, Michigan

FOREWORD

The United States program of development of atomic energy has been described by Major General L. R. Groves, who, as Commanding General of the War Department's Manhattan Project, directed the program from mid-1942 until December 31, 1946, as "a generation of scientific development compressed into three years." The tremendous scope of the Manhattan Project Technical Section of the National Nuclear Energy Series, which has been in preparation since 1944, is a tribute to the unprecedented accomplishments of science, industry, government, labor, and the Army and Navy working together as a team. These volumes can be a firm foundation for the United States atomic energy program which, in the words of the Atomic Energy Act of 1946, is " . . . directed toward improving the public welfare, increasing the standard of living, strengthening free competition in private enterprise, and promoting world peace."

David E. Lilienthal, Chairman
U. S. Atomic Energy Commission

ACKNOWLEDGMENT

The Manhattan Project Technical Section of the National Nuclear Energy Series embodies results of work done in the nation's wartime atomic energy program by numerous contractors, including Columbia University. The arrangements for publication of the series volumes were effected by Columbia University, under a contract with the United States Atomic Energy Commission. The Commission, for itself and for the other contractors who contributed to this series, wishes to record here its appreciation of this service of Columbia University in support of the national nuclear energy program.

PREFACE

This volume is one of a series which has been prepared as a record of the research work done under the Manhattan Project and the Atomic Energy Commission. The name Manhattan Project was assigned by the Corps of Engineers, War Department, to the far-flung scientific and engineering activities which had as their objective the utilization of atomic energy for military purposes. In the attainment of this objective, there were many developments in scientific and technical fields which are of general interest. The National Nuclear Energy Series (Manhattan Project Technical Section) is a record of these scientific and technical contributions, as well as of the developments in these fields which are being sponsored by the Atomic Energy Commission.

The declassified portion of the National Nuclear Energy Series, when completed, is expected to consist of some 60 volumes. These will be grouped into eight divisions, as follows:

Division   I — Electromagnetic Separation Project
Division   II — Gaseous Diffusion Project
Division   III — Special Separations Project
Division   IV — Plutonium Project
Division   V — Los Alamos Project
Division   VI — University of Rochester Project
Division VII — Materials Procurement Project
Division VIII — Manhattan Project

Soon after the close of the war the Manhattan Project was able to give its attention to the preparation of a complete record of the research work accomplished under Project contracts. Writing programs were authorized at all laboratories, with the object of obtaining complete coverage of Project results. Each major installation was requested to designate one or more representatives to make up a committee, which was first called the Manhattan Project Editorial Advisory Board, and later, after the sponsorship of the Series was assumed by the Atomic Energy Commission, the Project Editorial Advisory Board. This group made plans to coordinate the writing programs at all the installations, and acted as an advisory group in all matters affecting the Project-wide writing program. Its last meeting was held on Feb. 9, 1948, when it recommended the publisher for the Series.

The names of the Board members and of the installations which they represented are given below.

Atomic Energy Commission
   Public and Technical Information   Alberto F. Thompson
     Service

   Technical Information Branch,   Brewer F. Boardman
     Oak Ridge Extension

   Office of New York Operations   Charles Slesser, J. H. Hayner,
                                          W. M. Hearon *

Brookhaven National Laboratory   Richard W. Dodson

Carbide & Carbon Chemicals   R. B. Korsmeyer, W. L. Harwell,
   Corporation (K-25)   D. E. Hull, Ezra Staple

Carbide & Carbon Chemicals   Russell Baldock
   Corporation (Y-12) †

Clinton Laboratories ‡   J. R. Coe

General Electric Company, Hanford   T. W. Hauff

General Electric Company,   John P. Howe
   Knolls Atomic Power Laboratory

Kellex Corporation   John F. Hogerton, Jerome Simson,
                                        M. Benedict

Los Alamos   R. R. Davis, Ralph Carlisle Smith

National Bureau of Standards   C. J. Rodden

Plutonium Project
   Argonne National Laboratory   R. S. Mulliken, H. D. Young

   Iowa State College   F. H. Spedding

   Medical Group   R. E. Zirkle

SAM Laboratories §   G. M. Murphy

Stone & Webster Engineering   B. W. Whitehurst
   Corporation

University of California   R. K. Wakerling, A. Guthrie

University of Rochester   D. R. Charles, M. J. Wantman

* Represented Madison Square Area of the Manhattan District.
† The Y-12 plant at Oak Ridge was operated by Tennessee Eastman Corporation until May 4, 1947, at which time operations were taken over by Carbide & Carbon Chemicals Corporation.
‡ Clinton Laboratories was the former name of the Oak Ridge National Laboratory.
§ SAM (Substitute Alloy Materials) was the code name for the laboratories operated by Columbia University in New York under the direction of Dr. H. C. Urey, where much of the experimental work on isotope separation was done. On Feb. 1, 1945, the administration of these laboratories became the responsibility of Carbide & Carbon Chemicals Corporation. Research in progress there was transferred to the K-25 plant at Oak Ridge in June, 1946, and the New York laboratories were then closed.

Many difficulties were encountered in preparing a unified account
of Atomic Energy Project work. For example, the Project Editorial
Advisory Board was the first committee ever organized with representatives from every major installation of the Atomic Energy Project.
Compartmentation for security was so rigorous during the war that
it had been considered necessary to allow a certain amount of duplication of effort rather than to permit unrestricted circulation of
research information between certain installations. As a result, the
writing programs of different installations inevitably overlap markedly
in many scientific fields. The Editorial Advisory Board has exerted
itself to reduce duplication in so far as possible and to eliminate
discrepancies in factual data included in the volumes of the NNES.
In particular, unified Project-wide volumes have been prepared
on Uranium Chemistry and on the Analysis of Project Materials.
Nevertheless, the reader will find many instances of differences in
results or conclusions on similar subject matter prepared by different
authors. This has not seemed wholly undesirable for several reasons.
First of all, such divergencies are not unnatural and stimulate investigation. Second, promptness of publication has seemed more
important than the removal of all discrepancies. Finally, many Project scientists completed their contributions some time ago and have
become engrossed in other activities so that their time has not been
available for a detailed review of their work in relation to similar
work done at other installations.

The completion of the various individual volumes of the Series has
also been beset with difficulties. Many of the key authors and editors
have had important responsibilities in planning the future of atomic
energy research. Under these circumstances, the completion of this
technical series has been delayed longer than its editors wished. The
volumes are being released in their present form in the interest of
presenting the material as promptly as possible to those who can
make use of it.

The Editorial Advisory Board

LOS ALAMOS PROJECT FOREWORD

The volumes comprising the Los Alamos Division of the National Nuclear Energy Series represent only a fraction of the total documentation of the activities of the Los Alamos Scientific Laboratory since its establishment early in 1943. They were prepared originally as part of the Los Alamos Technical Series, a group of books intended as a comprehensive survey of the accomplishments of the Atomic Bomb Project. However, the necessary restrictions imposed on the dissemination of technical information affecting the nation's security have permitted the inclusion in the National Nuclear Energy Series of only that portion of the Los Alamos work which does not deal specifically with the nuclear weapon program.

Most of the volumes of the Los Alamos Technical Series were prepared late in 1945 and early in 1946, and because of the impossibility at that time of predicting the precise nature of a declassification policy that had not yet been formulated, they were written primarily as laboratory manuals intended for use by authorized staff members of the Laboratory and the Manhattan Project, rather than as books that might conceivably be made available to the general public at some unknown time in an obscure future. Despite the fact that a considerable portion of the work contained information of quite general scientific interest and had no obviously close connection with the design and construction of weapons, it has been a difficult, tedious, and unfinished task to extract such material from the existing volumes in order to create books of a publishable nature. In most cases, the Technical Series volumes were so written that the separation of unclassified from classified information requires a major rewriting and editing program, which is even further complicated because a number of the original authors and editors are no longer directly associated with the program of the Atomic Energy Commission.

Only one of the original volumes was written in such a manner that a substantial proportion might be declassified with minor deletions and revision. It bore the title "Experimental Techniques," and was divided into three main parts, each of which seemed of sufficient length to justify being made into a separate volume for inclusion in the National Nuclear Energy Series. These were (1) "Electronics" by William C. Elmore and Matthew L. Sands, (2) "Ionization Chambers and Counters" by Bruno B. Rossi and Hans H. Staub, and (3)

"Miscellaneous Physical and Chemical Techniques" by Alvin C. Graves et al. These now will appear as the first published volumes of the Los Alamos part of the National Nuclear Energy Series. Darol K. Froman, one of the originators of the Los Alamos Technical Series and editor of the original volume on "Experimental Techniques," has served as volume editor for each of these three divisional books.

Robert R. Davis
Ralph Carlisle Smith

June, 1949

PREFACE TO THE "EXPERIMENTAL TECHNIQUES" VOLUMES OF DIVISION V

In the late summer of 1945 it appeared likely that many of the electronic circuits and experimental techniques that were employed in what is now known as the Los Alamos Scientific Laboratory would be of appreciable value to the scientific world outside the Los Alamos Laboratory. Moreover, it was already apparent that many of the physicists, chemists, and engineers most prolific in devising circuits and techniques would not remain indefinitely with the Laboratory. Thus, for the sake of the history of accomplishment in the Laboratory, the inheritors of the physical plant, and the general scientific community, it became necessary to record in intelligible form some of the practices that were found most useful.

After much discussion it was decided that the only feasible approach to this problem must be made with the purely utilitarian objective of producing a laboratory manual. We decided to write down how to do things we knew how to do. In the great majority of these cases the "know how" was the result of experimentation and thought by many members of the laboratory staff, and very frequently fundamental ingredients were imported from the vast fields of common scientific knowledge, from other laboratories associated with the Manhattan Engineer District, and from other wartime projects. In particular, a large number of the electronic circuits involve fundamental elements or ideas derived from the work carried on at the Radiation Laboratory at Massachusetts Institute of Technology. During the war years much of the work of the Laboratory was either described sketchily in local reports or not described at all. Under these conditions it was apparent that proper credit for the development of circuits or techniques could not be given to individuals or even to groups. Yet it was felt that the value of a systematic recording would outweigh any demerit arising from an unorthodox omission of references. The work is not written completely without references but, in general, references are given only when it is thought that they would be of distinct aid to the reader. These are our excuses and apologies for omission of recognition to the hundreds of investigators whose work made these volumes possible.

Preparation for the writing was begun by circularizing the Laboratory for topics that should be included and indexing the topics. About this time the plan of writing the Los Alamos Technical Series was given considerable momentum, and the present work naturally became part of that series. The magnitude of the job became apparent at about the same time, and the authors of the various chapters were persuaded to undertake the task. In each case an author was selected for his intimate knowledge of the material and of the accomplishments of the Laboratory in the field. In every case at least some of the developments described are attributable directly to the authors. Little attempt has been made to make the various chapters uniform in mode of presentation since the clarity might have been impaired by altering the presentation of the authors.

We wish to express our appreciation for the efforts of the Laboratory's Declassification Section and Patent Group in expediting the release of the information in the present volumes on "Experimental Techniques." Since many of the developments appeared in writing for the first time in the manuscripts of these volumes, the job of tracing a device or part back to its inventor and writing adequate patent applications was a very major undertaking. Obviously the work could not be released until it was carefully reviewed to protect the interests of the U.S. Government.

The preparation of these volumes of Division V of the Manhattan Project Technical Section was encouraged in every possible way by the administration of the Laboratory under the direction first of J. Robert Oppenheimer and second of Norris E. Bradbury.

The work on "Experimental Techniques" is divided into three volumes by subject matter and for ease in binding. It may be that many readers will want only one volume, and for this reason some items are duplicated in different volumes. Also, an attempt has been made to keep cross-references to a minimum.

It is our earnest hope that these volumes will be found of practical value to experimentalists, particularly nuclear physicists, in spite of the fact that many of the techniques and circuits are now well known and some are even obsolescent.

Darol Froman
Los Alamos Scientific Laboratory

June, 1949

AUTHORS' PREFACE

The first four chapters of this volume deal with the fundamental features of ionization and the general properties of detectors based upon the ionization process. The last five chapters describe the construction of some typical detectors and their operation. Most of the detectors described were developed at the Los Alamos Laboratory, a few at other projects connected with the development of the atomic bomb. This is not intended to be a complete list of all detectors used at the Los Alamos project.

The material contained in this volume was collected with the help of many members of the Los Alamos staff. In particular, the authors wish to express their appreciation to F. C. Chromey and D. B. Nicodemus, who are responsible for compiling a large part of the information presented and who contributed valuable discussion.

Bruno B. Rossi
Hans H. Staub

June, 1949

The Manhattan Project Technical Section of the National Nuclear Energy Series is intended to be a comprehensive account of the scientific and technical achievements of the United States program for the development of atomic energy. It is not intended to be a detailed documentary record of the making of any inventions that happen to be mentioned in it. Therefore, the dates used in the Series should be regarded as a general temporal frame of reference, rather than as establishing dates of conception of inventions, of their reduction to practice, or of occasions of first use. While a reasonable effort has been made to assign credit fairly in the NNES volumes, this may, in many cases, be given to a group identified by the name of its leader rather than to an individual who was an actual inventor.

CONTENTS

CONTENTS

CHAPTER 9

Chapter 1

BEHAVIOR OF FREE ELECTRONS AND IONS IN GASES*

1.1 General Considerations. The ionization of a gas by an ionizing radiation, as is well-known, consists in the removal of one electron from each of a number of gas molecules. This changes the neutral molecules into positive ions. In some gases the electrons will remain free for a long time. In other gases they will, more or less promptly, attach themselves to neutral molecules forming heavy negative ions. It is also possible for an electron or a negative ion to recombine directly with a positive ion, giving rise to a neutral molecule. This phenomenon, however, will be of importance only in the regions of the gas where the ionization is very dense.

In an ionized gas not subject to any electric field, the electrons and ions will move at random, with an average energy of agitation equal to the average thermal translational energy of the gas molecules. This is given by $3kT/2$, where k is the Boltzmann constant. At a temperature of 15°C, $3kT/2$ is approximately equivalent to 3.7×10^{-2} ev. When an electric field is present, the electrons and ions, while still moving at random through the gas, will in addition undergo a general drift in a direction parallel to the electric field. At the same time their agitation energy will be increased above the thermal value $3kT/2$.

The average energy of electrons or ions when an electric field is present is generally measured by its ratio ϵ to the thermal agitation energy at 15°C. It may be characterized also by giving the root-mean-square velocity of agitation, u. The relation between ϵ and u is obviously

$$\epsilon \left(\frac{3kT}{2} \right) = \frac{mu^2}{2} \tag{1}$$

*The discussion presented in this chapter follows to some extent that given in R. H. Healey and J. W. Reed, "The Behavior of Slow Electrons in Gases," Amalgamated Wireless,Ltd., Sidney, 1941.

where m is the mass of the particle under consideration. It may be noted here that for positive or negative ions in an electric field, the average energy of agitation is always very close to the thermal value, while for electrons it is often considerably larger. The actual value of ϵ in a given gas and with a given electric field is determined by an equilibrium condition between the energy supplied by the electric field to the charged particles per unit time and that lost by these particles through collisions with the gas molecules.

The phenomenon of the attachment of electrons to neutral gas molecules mentioned above can be described by the attachment coefficient α, giving the probability of attachment per unit time. The coefficient α depends on the nature of the gas and on the energy distribution of the electrons. For a given gas and a given energy distribution, it is proportional to the number of collisions per second; i.e., it is proportional to the pressure.

The probability for an electron (or a negative ion) to recombine with a positive ion in a given time interval is clearly proportional to the density of positive ions. Thus the number of recombination processes per unit volume and unit time is given by the expression

$$\beta \, n^+ n^-$$

where n^+ and n^- are the densities of positive ions and of electrons (or negative ions), respectively. The quantity β will be called the recombination constant. Its value depends on the nature of the particles that recombine as well as on their agitation energy.

1.2 The Diffusion Equation for Ions and Electrons in a Gas. The motion of the electrons and ions through the gas, as determined by the action of the electric field and by the collisions with the gas molecules, can be described by a diffusion equation. In the absence of an electric field, this equation has the following form:

$$\vec{j} = -D \, \mathrm{grad} \, n \qquad (2)$$

where n is the density of particles in question, D is the so-called "diffusion coefficient," $\vec{j}$ is the current vector or, more accurately, the density vector for the material current, the magnitude of which gives the net number of particles per second crossing a surface of unit area perpendicular to its direction. The product of $\vec{j}$ times the electric charge of each particle (+e or −e) gives the density of electric current. Whether an electric field is present or not, the collisions of electrons and ions with gas molecules are so frequent, or, in other words, the diffusion coefficient is so small, that the "transport velocity," defined as $\vec{j}/n$, is always very small compared with the velocity of agitation, u.

We want now to write the expression for $\vec{j}$ in the case where an electric field is present. For the sake of simplicity, assume that the field is uniform. Then for any type of charged particle the average energy of agitation and the diffusion coefficient (which is a function of the energy of agitation) are also constant in space.

The equation required can be obtained by considering the momentum balance in a volume element within the ionized gas. The total momentum of the charged particles in the volume element under consideration is modified (1) by the action of the electric field on the charged particles, (2) by the collisions of the charged particles with gas molecules, and (3) by exchange of charged particles with neighboring elements. The rate of change of the momentum per unit volume due to the electric field is $ne\vec{E}$, where $\vec{E}$ is the electric field strength; that caused by loss through collisions will be denoted by $-\vec{M}$. In order to calculate the rate of exchange of momentum with the neighboring elements, let us consider a surface element dS in the ionized gas and a unit vector $\vec{a}$ perpendicular to dS. If we consider the absolute value of $\vec{j}$ as negligible compared with nu and assume for a moment that all the charged particles under consideration have the same velocity of agitation u, the number of particles per second crossing dS and moving at angles between θ and $\theta + d\theta$ with respect to $\vec{a}$ is given by

$$\tfrac{1}{2} nu \cos \theta \sin \theta \, dS \, d\theta$$

The total momentum carried by these particles is, for reason of symmetry, in the direction of $\vec{a}$ and has a value

$$(\tfrac{1}{2} nu \cos \theta \sin \theta \, dS \, d\theta) \, mu \cos \theta$$

Integration over θ from 0 to π gives the following expression for the increase of momentum per unit time on that side of dS toward which the vector $\vec{a}$ is pointing

$$\tfrac{1}{3} nmu^2 \, \vec{a} \, dS$$

Hence the rate of increase of momentum in a volume A bounded by a closed surface S has the expression

$$\int_S \tfrac{1}{3} nmu^2 \, \vec{a} \, dS = - \int_A \tfrac{1}{3} mu^2 \, \text{grad } n \, dA$$

from which it follows that the rate of change of momentum per unit volume is

$$-\tfrac{1}{3} mu^2 \, \text{grad } n$$

This expression is valid also if the charged particles do not all have the same velocity of agitation, provided one considers u as the root-mean-square velocity. The principle of conservation of momentum is then expressed by the following equation

$$ne\vec{E} - \tfrac{1}{3}mu^2 \ \text{grad} \ n - \vec{M} = \frac{d(m\vec{j})}{dt}$$

The quantity on the right-hand side of the above equation represents the rate of change of the net momentum of the charged particles contained in the unit volume. Its value depends on the value of the diffusion coefficient D. The left-hand side of the equation contains terms (like $ne\vec{E}$) which do not depend on D. In most practical cases, D is so small that $d(m\vec{j})/dt$ is negligible compared with the terms on the left-hand side of the equation (just as the transport velocity $\vec{j}/n$ is negligible compared with the agitation velocity u). Therefore the equation above may be written as

$$ne\vec{E} - \tfrac{1}{3} mu^2 \ \text{grad} \ n = \vec{M} \qquad (3)$$

In order to determine $\vec{M}$, note that $\vec{M}$, by its nature, must be a definite function of $\vec{j}$, independent of whether the current that $\vec{j}$ represents is produced by a gradient of the density or by an electric field. The form of this function can therefore be determined by Eqs. 2 and 3 under the assumption $\vec{E} = 0$. Thus

$$\vec{M} = \frac{1}{3} \frac{mu^2}{D} \vec{j} \qquad (4)$$

With this expression for $\vec{M}$, Eq. 3 becomes

$$\vec{j} = -D \ \text{grad} \ n + \frac{3D}{mu^2} \ ne\vec{E} \qquad (5)$$

The drift produced by the electric field is best described by the drift velocity $\vec{w}$, which is defined as the velocity of the center of gravity of the charged particles in the uniform electric field.*

---

*The drift velocity $\vec{w}$ may also be defined as the average vector velocity of all charged particles under consideration, as opposed to the transport velocity $\vec{j}/n$, which represents the average velocity of the particles contained in a volume element at a given point of the gas.

According to this definition, $\vec{w}$ is given by the equation

$$\vec{w} = \frac{\int_A \vec{j}\ dA}{\int_A n\ dA} \tag{6}$$

where the integrations are extended over a volume that contains all the particles under consideration. Since n is zero at the surface that limits this volume, $\int_A$ grad n dA is zero. It then follows that

$$\vec{w} = \frac{3D}{mu^2}\ e\vec{E} \tag{7}$$

or, from Eq. 1

$$\vec{w} = \frac{D}{\epsilon kT}\ e\vec{E} \tag{7a}$$

Equation 5 can now be rewritten as

$$\vec{j} = -D\ \mathrm{grad}\ n + n\vec{w} \tag{8}$$

Consider a region of the gas where no ions or electrons are formed and none disappear by attachment or recombination. In this region the number of particles of each type is conserved, and the following equation holds:

$$\frac{\partial n}{\partial t} = -\mathrm{div}\ \vec{j} \tag{9}$$

which together with Eq. 8 gives

$$\frac{\partial n}{\partial t} = D\ \mathrm{div}\ \mathrm{grad}\ n - \mathrm{div}\ (n\vec{w}) \tag{10}$$

This equation will be applied to the problem of determining the motion of a number of particles produced in a very small volume at the time t = 0. Mathematically, this means solving Eq. 10 with the condition that the solution should become a δ function for t = 0.

Writing Eq. 10 in cartesian coordinates with the z axis in the direction of w and introducing the new variable

$$z' = z - wt$$

we obtain the ordinary diffusion equation without convection. The solution of this equation for the boundary condition indicated is well-known.* Expressed in terms of the original variables, it reads

$$n(x, y, z, t) = \frac{N}{\left[\sqrt{2\,\pi}\, l(t) \right]^3} e^{-[x^2 + y^2 + (z - wt)^2]/2l^2(t)} \qquad (11)$$

where N is the total number of particles and

$$l^2(t) = 2Dt \qquad (12)$$

Physically, the solution represented by Eq. 11 indicates that the particles, originally contained in an infinitesimal volume at the origin of the coordinate system, drift with an average velocity $\vec{w}$ in the direction of the positive z axis and at the same time spread into a cloud which becomes increasingly diffused as time goes on. The length l represents the root-mean-square distance of the particles from any plane through the center of gravity of the cloud at the time t. Equation 12 shows that l increases as the square root of the time.

1.3 Mean Free Path; Energy Loss per Collision; Mixture of Gases. The drift velocity is often expressed in terms of the mean free path between collisions of the charged particles with gas molecules. This mean free path is inversely proportional to the pressure. Its value at the pressure p will be indicated by λ/p, where λ is the mean free path at unit pressure. The relation between $\vec{w}$ and λ/p can be determined easily if one makes two crude simplifying assumptions: (1) all the particles under consideration have the same agitation velocity u; (2) the direction of the motion of the particle after the collision is completely independent of the direction of its motion before the collision. Under these assumptions, each particle undergoes on the average $(u \times p)/\lambda$ collisions per second, in which it loses on the average a momentum equal to $(u \times p/\lambda)m\vec{w}$. On the other hand, each particle gains every second a momentum equal to $e\vec{E}$ through the action of the

*See, for instance, Slater and Frank, "Introduction to Theoretical Physics," McGraw-Hill Book Company, Inc., New York, 1933.

electric field. Hence, once equilibrium is established, the following equation holds:

$$\frac{upm\vec{w}}{\lambda} = e\vec{E} \tag{13}$$

or

$$w = \frac{e}{m}\frac{\lambda}{u}\frac{\vec{E}}{p} \tag{14}$$

Similarly, one may express the mean agitation energy ϵ in terms of λ and of the average fractional energy loss per collision, which can be indicated by h. The principle of conservation of energy gives the equation

$$\epsilon \left(\frac{3kT}{2}\right) \left(\frac{up}{\lambda}\right) h = e\vec{E} \cdot \vec{w} \tag{15}$$

It is well-known, of course, that neither of the two conditions (1) and (2) mentioned above corresponds to reality. However, λ and h can be considered as two quantities that are defined in terms of experimental quantities by Eqs. 13 and 15 and are representative of the momentum loss and of the energy loss through collisions. If we take this view, Eq. 13 states the obvious fact that the momentum loss per second through collisions is proportional to the pressure and to the drift velocity, and for a given pressure and drift velocity depends on the nature of the gas and on the energy distribution of the particles under consideration. Similarly Eq. 15 indicates merely that the energy loss per second through collisions is proportional to the pressure and that this loss depends on the nature of the gas and the energy distribution of the particles.

In practice, λ and h can be determined as a function of ϵ for a given gas by measuring $\vec{w}$ and ϵ as a function of E/p. Equations 13 and 1 will then provide the functional relation between λ and ϵ, while Eqs. 15 and 1 will provide that between h/λ and ϵ.

The quantities λ and h are particularly useful in connection with the problem of determining the behavior of electrons and ions in a mixture of gases from data relative to their behavior in the pure components. For this purpose assume that the energy distribution of the charged particles, whether in a mixture of gases or in any pure gas, is completely determined by their average energy ϵ. It is difficult to justify this hypothesis, but it seems to lead to results in agreement with the experimental data.

Let p_0 be the total gas pressure and let p_1, p_2, p_3, etc., be the partial pressures of the various components. Similarly, let λ_0 and h_0 be the values of λ and h for the mixture, let λ_1, λ_2, λ_3, etc., and h_1, h_2, h_3, etc., be the values of the same quantities for the various components. If the average momentum loss and the average energy loss of electrons or ions in the mixture are considered equal, respectively, to the sum of the average momentum losses and to the sum of the average energy losses in the separate components, we obtain from Eqs. 13 and 15 the following equations (after dividing each equation by a factor, which is the same for all terms since it depends only on $\overrightarrow{w}$, m, and u):

$$\frac{p_0}{\lambda_0} = \frac{p_1}{\lambda_1} + \frac{p_2}{\lambda_2} + \frac{p_3}{\lambda_3} + \cdots$$

(16)

$$\frac{p_0 h_0}{\lambda_0} = \frac{p_1 h_1}{\lambda_1} + \frac{p_2 h_2}{\lambda_2} + \frac{p_3 h_3}{\lambda_3} + \cdots$$

After λ_0 and h_0 have been calculated by Eq. 16, Eqs. 13 and 15 can be used to compute ϵ and $\overrightarrow{w}$ as functions of E/p for the mixture.

The diffusion coefficient too may be expressed in terms of λ. A comparison of Eqs. 14 and 7 gives the well-known relation

$$D = \frac{\lambda u}{3p}$$

(17)

So far we have assumed that the electric field is uniform. If the field is not uniform but does not vary appreciably over a distance of the order of one mean free path, we may still define an average agitation energy ϵ. This quantity, however, as well as all the quantities that depend on ϵ, such as D, λ, and h, will vary from point to point. The fundamental Eq. 8 will still hold, provided the current produced by the gradient of temperature is negligible compared with that produced by the electric field or by the gradient of density.

Another question concerns the time interval between the moment when the ions are produced and the moment when they reach the equilibrium condition between loss and gain of momentum, which leads to Eq. 8. This time is of the order of the time between collisions, λ/pu, which at atmospheric pressure is generally between 10^{-11} and 10^{-12} sec.

In Table 1.1 are listed the symbols for the most important quantities defined above, along with the units in which they are measured.

1.4 Experimental Data on Free Electrons. Equation 14 indicates that the drift velocity is a function of the ratio E/p. Experimental determinations of the drift velocity of electrons confirm this fact.

Table 1.1—List of Symbols

Symbol	Quantity	Unit
u	Root-mean-square velocity of agitation	Cm/sec
ϵ	Average agitation energy	$3kT/2 = 3.7 \times 10^{-2}$ev (at 15°C)
w	Drift velocity	Cm/sec
D	Diffusion coefficient	Sq cm/sec
p	Pressure	Mm Hg
λ	Mean free path at 1 mm Hg	Cm·(mm Hg)
h	Fractional energy loss per collision	Dimensionless
α	Attachment coefficient	Per sec
β	Recombination constant	Cu cm/sec
E/p	Field strength per unit pressure	Volts/cm·(mm Hg)

The dependence of w on E/p is given for a number of different gases in Figs. 1.1 to 1.6. Most of the data used in the construction of these graphs were taken from Healey and Reed, "The Behavior of Slow Electrons in Gases," where various methods for the measurement of w, ϵ, and α are described. In Fig. 1.3 the Los Alamos data at p = 840 mm Hg were obtained from observation of α-particle pulses, as described in Chap. 3, Sec. 3.8. Their accuracy was estimated to be about

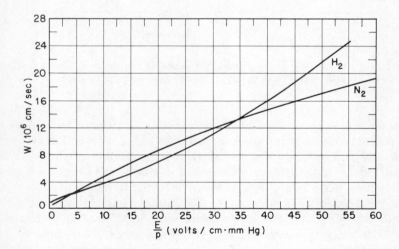

Fig. 1.1—Drift velocity of electrons as a function of E/p in H₂ and N₂ (Townsend and Bailey, in Healey and Reed, pp. 92 and 93).

20 per cent. The data at p = 1,274 mm Hg were obtained by means of the pulsed x-ray source, as described in Chap. 3, Sec. 3.8. Their accuracy was estimated to be about 5 per cent. The disagreement

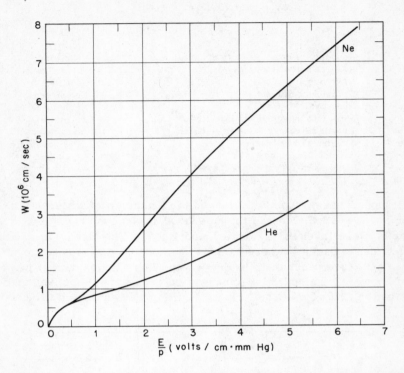

Fig. 1.2—Drift velocity of electrons as a function of E/p in He and in Ne containing 1 per cent of He (Townsend and Bailey, in Healey and Reed, pp. 89 and 90).

between the various sets of measurements is striking and not easily explained, especially if compared with the agreement obtained for CO_2 with different methods (see Fig. 1.4). It is possible that it may be due, in part at least, to different degrees of purity of the gases used, since the drift velocity in argon is strongly affected by impurities.

In the data obtained with argon-CO_2 mixtures and shown in Fig. 1.6, it will be seen that, for a given value of E/p (at least up to E/p $\approx$ 3), the drift velocity in a mixture containing a large proportion of argon and a small proportion of CO_2 is considerably greater than in either pure argon or pure CO_2 (see Figs. 1.3 and 1.4). This fact, which was established through experiments carried out at Los Alamos, is of considerable practical importance for the construction of "fast" chambers. The physical reason for it can be understood through the following analysis.

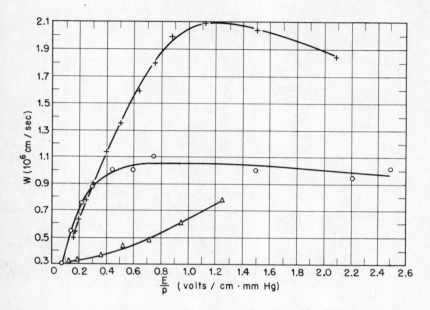

Fig. 1.3—Drift velocity of electrons as a function of E/p in argon. △, Townsend and Bailey, in Healey and Reed, p. 91; ○ , Los Alamos, p = 840 mm Hg; +, Los Alamos, p = 1,274 mm Hg. The Los Alamos data were obtained partly from observation of α-particle pulses and partly by means of the pulsed x-ray source, as described in Chap. 3, Sec. 3.8.

Inelastic collisions between electrons and gas molecules occur only when the electrons have an energy larger than the energy of the first excitation level of the molecule. Argon is a monatomic gas, and the first excitation level of the argon atom is 11.5 ev. Hence in pure argon, even with moderate fields, the electrons will reach a very high agitation energy — of the order of 10 ev or $\epsilon \approx 300$. This is confirmed by direct measurements, as shown in Fig. 1.9. In CO_2, however, inelastic collisions occur very frequently for small electron energies, because of the large number of low excitation levels of the CO_2 molecule. It follows that the addition of a small amount of CO_2 to argon will reduce the average energy of the electrons considerably. Calculations show, for instance, that with 10 per cent CO_2 and E/p = 1 this energy drops from about 10 ev to about 1 ev. In a mixture containing only a small amount of CO_2, the drift velocity is limited mainly by the collisions with the argon molecules. The mean free path of electrons in argon increases rapidly with decreasing energy in the region between

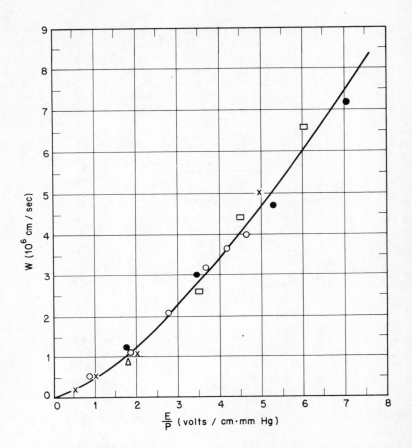

Fig. 1.4—Drift velocity of electrons as a function of E/p in CO_2. □ , Rudd (see Healey and Reed, p. 98); ×, Skinker (see Healey and Reed, p. 99); △, Los Alamos, p = 660 mm Hg; ○ , Los Alamos, p = 305 mm Hg; ● , Los Alamos, p = 160 mm Hg. The Los Alamos data were obtained from observation of α-particle pulses as described in Chap. 3, Sec. 3.8.

10 and 1 ev, a phenomenon known as the Ramsauer effect. Since the drift velocity is directly proportional to the mean free path and inversely proportional to the square root of the agitation energy (see Eq. 14), the decrease of the latter quantity caused by addition of CO_2 to argon will result, in two ways, in an increase of the drift velocity. The experimental values of drift velocities are by no means as accurate as one would desire. This applies also to the values obtained

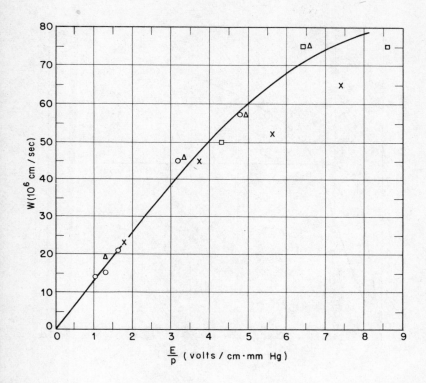

Fig. 1.5—Drift velocity of electrons as a function of E/p in BF_3. $\triangle$, BF_3 from C_6H_5-N_2BF_4, p = 379 mm Hg; $\bigcirc$, BF_3 from tank, p = 388 mm Hg; $\times$, BF_3 from $C_6H_5N_2BF_4$, p = 339 mm Hg; $\square$, BF_3 from tank, p = 294 mm Hg. The data were obtained from observation of α-particle pulses as described in Chap. 3, Sec. 3.8.

recently at the Los Alamos Laboratories. Here the pressure under which work was conducted made it impossible to carry out measurements of high precision when high precision was not needed for the immediate objective to be achieved. It is felt, however, that the methods developed at Los Alamos (Chap. 3, Sec. 3.8), when properly applied would be capable of yielding accurate results.

The average agitation energy ϵ, according to Eq. 15, is also a function of E/p. Figures 1.7 to 1.10 give the dependence of ϵ on E/p for free electrons and for a number of different gases. The experimental data were taken from Healey and Reed.

The attachment coefficient α is practically zero for H_2, He, A, N, and CO_2 if these gases are sufficiently pure. Some experimental data

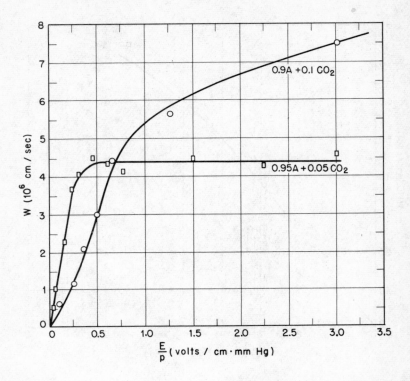

Fig. 1.6—Drift velocity of electrons as a function of E/p in mixtures of argon and CO_2. The data were obtained from observation of α-particle pulses as described in Chap. 3, Sec. 3.8.

on the attachment of electrons in two of the most common impurities, namely O_2 and H_2O, are summarized in Fig. 1.11. The ordinates in this figure give the ratio α/pw that represents the probability for electrons to attach themselves to a gas molecule while traveling 1 cm in the direction of the field in the gas at 1 mm Hg of pressure.

No reliable data on the recombination of electrons with positive ions are available. According to Kenty, as quoted by Loeb, the approximate value of the recombination constant for electrons in argon is

$$\beta = 2 \times 10^{-10} \text{ cu cm/sec}$$

The values of β for other gases do not seem to differ materially from that relative to argon. It must be pointed out here that the ions

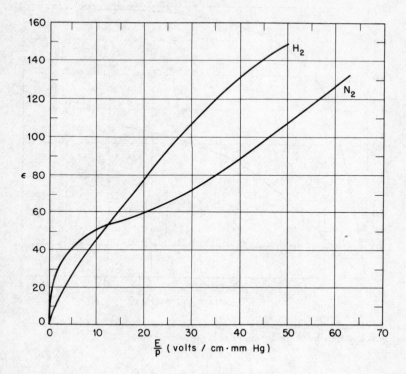

Fig. 1.7—Mean agitation energy of electrons as a function of E/p for H_2 and N_2 (Townsend and Bailey, in Healey and Reed, pp. 92 and 93).

are seldom uniformly distributed in the volume of the gas. This is especially true when the ionization is produced by heavily ionizing particles like α particles. In this case, of course, the actual density of positive ions at the place where electrons are present determines the recombination rate, and this density may be considerably higher than the average volume density, at least as long as electrons and positive ions have not diffused sufficiently far from the place where they have both been produced. The recombination of positive ions with electrons (or negative ions), which takes place before diffusion spreads these particles apart, is often referred to as "preferential recombination," or "columnar recombination."

The root-mean-square velocity of agitation u, the diffusion coefficient D, the mean free path λ, and the fractional energy loss per

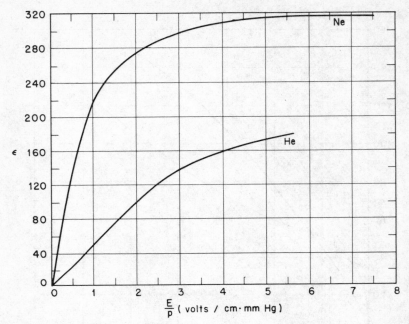

Fig. 1.8—Mean agitation energy of electrons as a function of E/p for He and Ne (Townsend and Bailey, in Healey and Reed, pp. 89 and 90).

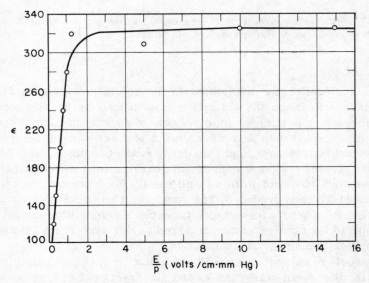

Fig. 1.9—Mean agitation energy of electrons as a function of E/p for argon (Townsend and Bailey, in Healey and Reed, p. 91).

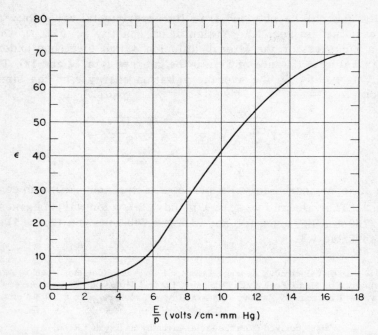

Fig. 1.10 — Mean agitation energy of electrons as a function of E/p for CO_2 (Rudd and Skinker, in Healey and Reed, pp. 98 and 99).

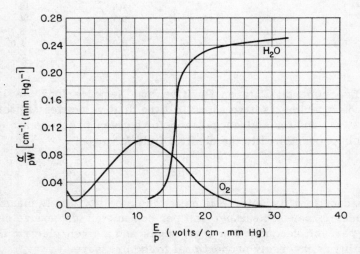

Fig. 1.11 — Probability for electron attachment per centimeter path at 1 mm Hg as a function of E/p in O_2 and H_2O (Healey and Kirkpatrick, Bailey and Duncanson, in Healey and Reed, pp. 94 and 99).

collision h can all be obtained from the experimental values of w and ϵ, as explained in Sec. 1.3. A significant quantity is $\sqrt{2D/w}$, which gives a measure for the lateral diffusion which electrons undergo while traveling a distance of 1 cm in the gas (see Eqs. 11 and 12). This quantity is related to the average agitation energy ϵ by the simple equation

$$\sqrt{\frac{2D}{w}} = \sqrt{\frac{2kT\epsilon}{eE}} = \sqrt{\frac{5 \times 10^{-2}}{E}} \sqrt{\epsilon} \qquad (18)$$

where E is measured in volts per centimeter and $\sqrt{2D/w}$ in centimeters $^{\frac{1}{2}}$. The values of w, ϵ, u, λ/p and $\sqrt{2D/w}$ for various gases at 1 atm (760 mm Hg) pressure and with E = 760 volts/cm (E/p = 1) are listed in Table 1.2.

Table 1.2—Drift Velocity (w), Average Agitation Energy (ϵ), Root-mean-square Agitation Velocity (u), Mean Free Path (λ/p), and Lateral Diffusion per Centimeter Path ($\sqrt{2D/w}$) for Electrons in Various Gases at 1 Atm Pressure, with E = 760 Volts/cm (E/p = 1)

(Values derived from the tables given by Healey and Reed)

Gas	w(10^6 cm/sec)	ϵ	u(10^6 cm/sec)	$\lambda/p(10^{-4}$ cm)	$\sqrt{2D/w}$ (10^{-2} cm$^{\frac{1}{2}}$)
H_2	1.2	9.3	35	0.3	2.5
He	0.8	53	84	0.5	6
Ne	1.2	214	168	1.5	12
A	0.6	287	195	0.9	14
N_2	0.9	21.5	53	0.3	3.7
CO_2	0.55	1.5	14	0.06	1.0

1.5 **Experimental Data on Positive and Negative Ions.** A large number of experiments have shown that the drift velocities of positive and negative ions for a given gas and for a given pressure are quite accurately proportional to the electric field strength:

$$\vec{w} = \mu\vec{E} \qquad (19)$$

The proportionality factor μ is called the mobility, and is measured in centimeters per second, per volt per centimeter (or square centimeters per volt second). For a given gas and a given electric field, the mobility is inversely proportional to the pressure.

The values of μ for positive ions in a number of gases are listed in Table 1.3.* The mobilities of negative ions, when negative ions exist, are nearly equal to, but generally are slightly larger than, those of the corresponding positive ions.

Table 1.3—Mobilities and Diffusion Coefficients of Positive Ions in Various Gases at 1 Atm Pressure (p = 760 mm Hg)

	H_2	He	A	N_2	O_2	CO_2	Air	Ethane
μ (sq cm/volt sec)	5−6	5.1	1.3	1.3	1.3	0.8	1.3−1.4	1.07 (negative ions)
D (10^{-2} sq cm/sec)	12			3	2.5−3.0	2.5	2.8	

The diffusion coefficient D, according to Eq. 7a, is related to the mobility μ by the equation

$$D = \frac{\epsilon kT}{e} \mu \qquad (20)$$

Since $kT/e = 2.5 \times 10^{-2}$ volt and ϵ is always close to 1, for positive or negative ions,

$$D = 2.5 \times 10^{-2} \mu \text{ sq cm/sec} \qquad (21)$$

In Table 1.3 some experimental values of D at 1 atm pressure are listed along with the corresponding values of μ.† Because of the moderate accuracy in the measurements of both D and μ, Eq. 21 may be considered as fairly well verified.

The data on the recombination of positive and negative ions are very inaccurate. For most gases the values of the recombination constant β seem to be between 1 and 2 times 10^{-6} cu cm/sec, which is about 10^4 times larger than the recombination constant between positive ions and electrons.

*These values were taken from the article by Loeb in "International Critical Tables," 1929, Vol. VI, p. 111.
†"International Critical Tables," Vol. VI, p. 115.

Chapter 2

OPERATION OF IONIZATION CHAMBERS
WITH CONSTANT IONIZATION

2.1 General Design of an Ionization Chamber. The essential parts of an ionization chamber are two electrodes kept at different potentials and a gas that fills the space between the two electrodes. The electrode to which the measuring instrument is attached is called the collecting electrode. The collecting electrode is ordinarily, but not necessarily, at a potential close to ground potential. The other electrode, which is ordinarily kept at a constant voltage V_0 of several hundred to several thousand volts, is called the high-voltage electrode. The collecting electrode is usually supported through insulators by another electrode which is held at a constant voltage, approximately equal to that of the collecting electrode itself. This is called the guard electrode. The guard electrode, in turn, is connected through insulators to the high-voltage electrode. The purpose of the guard electrode is to prevent leakage currents from reaching the collecting electrode. Also, the guard electrode is usually so shaped as to prevent irregularities of the electric field near the edges of the collecting electrode. The general design of an ionization chamber is schematically represented in Fig. 2.1.

Let us consider the volume limited by the surface of the collecting electrode, the tube of force passing through the periphery of the collecting electrode, and that portion of the high-voltage electrode which is intercepted by this tube of force. This volume will be called the sensitive volume of the chamber. Every ion of sign opposite to that of the collecting electrode formed within the sensitive volume will reach the collecting electrode, provided diffusion and recombination can be neglected.

2.2 Constant Ionization: Diffusion and Recombination Neglected. Assume now that the ionization chamber is irradiated with a source of ionization of constant intensity, and let $n_0(x,y,z)$ be the number of ion pairs produced per unit volume and per unit time at the point (x,y,z). Let $n^+(x,y,z)$ and $n^-(x,y,z)$ be the densities of positive and negative carriers, respectively. Let $\vec{w}^+$ (x,y,z) and $\vec{w}^-$ (x,y,z) be their drift velocities. For the sake of simplicity, assume that the negative carriers are all of one kind, i.e., either free electrons (no attachment)

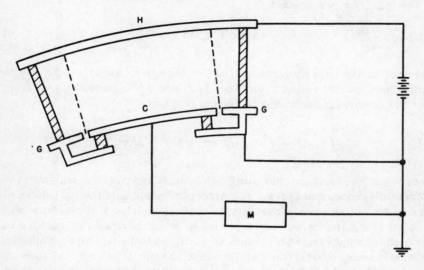

Fig. 2.1—Schematic diagram of an ionization chamber. H, high-voltage electrode; C, collecting electrode; G, guard electrode; M, measuring instrument.

or negative ions (complete attachment). Neglecting diffusion, the current vectors for the positive and negative particles are given by

$$\vec{j}^+ = n^+\vec{w}^+, \quad \vec{j}^- = n^-\vec{w}^- \tag{1}$$

Assuming that no recombination takes place,

$$\text{div } \vec{j}^+ = \text{div } \vec{j}^- = n_0 \tag{2}$$

The density of electric current can be expressed as

$$e\vec{j} = e(\vec{j}^+ - \vec{j}^-) = e(n^+\vec{w}^+ - n^-\vec{w}^-) \tag{3}$$

and from Eq. 2 it follows that

$$\text{div } \vec{j} = 0 \tag{4}$$

Neglecting diffusion, $\vec{j}$ is parallel to the lines of force, and it follows from Eq. 4 that the total current through any surface intercepted by the lateral boundary of the sensitive volume has the same value I. This may be called the ionization current in the chamber. We may expect I to equal the product of e times the number of ion pairs formed in the chamber per second

$$I = e \int_A n_0 \, dA \tag{5}$$

where A is the sensitive volume of the chamber. Actually, Eq. 5 can easily be shown to follow from Eqs. 1, 2, and 3. Suppose, for instance, that the collecting electrode is negative. Then

$$\int_A n_0 \, dA = \int_A \operatorname{div}(n^+ \vec{w}^+) \, dA = \int_S n^+ \vec{w}_n^+ \, dS$$

where S is the surface that limits the sensitive volume and w_n^+ indicates the component of $\vec{w}^+$ in a direction perpendicular to this surface and pointing toward the outside of the sensitive volume. Now w_n^+ is zero along the lateral surface, while n^+ is zero on the surface of the high-voltage electrode, which is assumed to be positive. This can be easily understood from the fact that the positive ions, as soon as they are formed, drift away from the positive electrode and are not replaced by positive ions coming from behind this surface. For the same reason, n^- is zero at the surface of the collecting electrode. Hence, if S^- is the surface of the collecting electrode, then

$$e \int_A n_0 \, dA = e \int_{S^-} n^+ \vec{w}_n^+ \, dS = e \int_{S^-} \vec{j}_n \, dS$$

which proves Eq. 5.

Thus the problem of determining the ionization current when diffusion and recombination are neglected is a trivial one.

The next problem is that of determining, under the same assumptions, the space-charge distribution, which is defined by

$$\rho = e(n^+ - n^-) \tag{6}$$

For the determination of ρ we must consider, in addition to Eqs. 1, 2, and 6, the equations for the electric field strength

$$\operatorname{div} \vec{E} = 4\pi\rho \tag{7}$$

$$\operatorname{curl} \vec{E} = 0 \tag{8}$$

and the equations that relate $\vec{w}^+$ and $\vec{w}^-$ to $\vec{E}$.

The mathematical problem is generally rather involved. However, it becomes easy to handle in the case of certain simple geometries or when the density of ionization is sufficiently small so that it will not appreciably affect the field strength (and therefore the drift velocities).

Consider, for instance, a parallel plate chamber. Assume that its collecting electrode is surrounded by an appropriate guard electrode so that the electric field is practically uniform up to the boundary of the sensitive volume. Take as a frame of reference a cartesian coordinate system with its origin on the positive electrode and its x axis in the direction of the electric field. Suppose that the chamber is uniformly irradiated over the active volume and sufficiently beyond it so that any additional electric field produced by the space charge is also parallel to the x axis and independent of the y and z coordinates.

The problem then becomes one-dimensional and Eq. 2 can be integrated immediately. If Eq. 1 and the boundary conditions at the two electrodes are taken into account, then

$$n^+ w_x^+ = n^+ w^+ = n_0 x$$
$$-n^- w_x^- = n^- w^- = n_0(d - x)$$

(9)

where d is the separation of the electrodes and w^+ and w^- are the absolute values of the drift velocities. Equation 7 now becomes

$$\frac{dE}{dx} = 4\pi e n_0 \left(\frac{x}{w^+} - \frac{d - x}{w^-} \right)$$

(10)

If w^+ and w^- are known functions of E, Eq. 10 can be solved, at least in principle.

The problem can be simplified, since w^+ is proportional to E and so is w^- if the negative carriers are ions. In this case, by introducing the mobilities μ^+ and μ^-, Eq. 10 becomes

$$\frac{dE}{dx} = 4\pi e \frac{n_0}{E} \left(\frac{x}{\mu^+} - \frac{d - x}{\mu^-} \right)$$

(11)

which gives

$$E^2 + \text{const.} = 4\pi e n_0 \left[\frac{x^2}{\mu^+} + \frac{(d - x)^2}{\mu^-} \right]$$

(12)

where the constant is determined by the condition

$$\int_0^d E \, dx = V_0 \tag{13}$$

On the other hand, if the negative carriers are electrons, then w^- is of the order of $1,000 \, w^+$ and no large error is made by neglecting the second term in the parentheses of Eq. 10, so that

$$E^2 + \text{const.} = \frac{4\pi e n_0}{\mu^+} x^2 \tag{14}$$

The problem can be simplified further by assuming that the electric field produced by the space charge is small compared with the externally applied field; i.e.,

$$E = \frac{V_0}{d} + E_\rho$$

with

$$E_\rho \ll \frac{V_0}{d}$$

Equation 13 gives for E_ρ the condition $\int E_\rho \, dx = 0$.

Since w^+ and w^- are smooth functions of E and since E is approximately constant, w^+ and w^- can also be considered constant. If electron attachment takes place and the mobilities of positive and negative ions are assumed to be the same ($w^+ = w^- = w$), Eq. 10 yields

$$E_\rho = \frac{4\pi e n_0}{w} \left(x^2 - xd + \frac{d^2}{6} \right)$$

$$n^+ = \frac{n_0}{w} x$$

$$n^- = \frac{n_0}{w} (d - x) \tag{15}$$

$$\rho = e \frac{n_0}{w} (2x - d)$$

In the case of free electrons the solution is

$$E_\rho = \frac{2\pi e n_0}{w^+} \left(x^2 - \frac{d^2}{3}\right)$$

$$n^+ = \frac{n_0}{w^+} x$$

$$n^- = \frac{n_0}{w^-} (d - x) \approx 0 \tag{16}$$

$$\rho = e \frac{n_0}{w^+} x$$

2.3 Constant Ionization: Diffusion and Recombination Not Neglected.
If the diffusion is taken into account, then the expressions for the current vectors $\vec{j}^+$ and $\vec{j}^-$ are (see Chap. 1, Eq. 8).

$$\vec{j}^+ = n^+ \vec{w}^+ - D^+ \operatorname{grad} n^+$$
$$\vec{j}^- = n^- \vec{w}^- - D^- \operatorname{grad} n^- \tag{17}$$

and, if recombination is not neglected, Eq. 2 is replaced by

$$\operatorname{div} \vec{j}^+ = \operatorname{div} \vec{j}^- = n_0 - \beta n^+ n^- \tag{18}$$

In order to determine the boundary conditions at the electrodes assume that the reflection coefficient of the electrodes for electrons and ions is negligible, so that every charged particle that impinges upon a given electrode is captured. This assumption did not enter in the calculation of current in Sec. 2.2. In fact, when diffusion is negligible, ions of a given sign always end on the electrode of the opposite sign, even if some of them are reflected when they first impinge upon it. When the diffusion is appreciable, however, a certain number of ions return by diffusion to the electrode of the same sign. If some of these ions are reflected, the electric field will probably prevent them from reaching the same electrode again. On account of the small velocity of electrons and ions in gases, assuming the reflection coefficient to be negligible is probably justified in all practical cases.

Under this assumption, the number of electrons or ions that enter an electrode on account of their thermal agitation is proportional to the product of their density n at the electrode and their agitation velocity u (Chap. 1, Sec. 1.2). On the other hand, the diffusion coefficient D is proportional to the product of u and the mean free path λ (see Chap. 1, Eq. 17). The theory of motion for electrons and ions in a gas is usually developed for the limiting case of $\lambda = 0$. This corresponds to assuming $u = \infty$. Since the current is finite, the density of electrons and ions must be zero at the electrodes.

The density of electric current is still given by the equation

$$e\vec{j} = e(\vec{j}^+ - \vec{j}^-) \tag{19}$$

However, $\vec{j}$ is no longer parallel to the lines of force; hence the total electric current will no longer be the same across every surface intercepted by the lateral boundary of the sensitive volume. Nor will the current I through the measuring instrument still equal the total charge $e \int_A n_0 \, dA$ produced within the sensitive volume per unit time. If, for instance, the collecting electrode is negative, I is given by the expression

$$I = e \int_{S^-} (j_n^+ - j_n^-) \, dS = e \int_A n_0 \, dA - e \int_A \beta n^+ n^- \, dA - e \int_{S^-} j_n^- \, dS$$

$$- e \int_{S^+} j_n^+ \, dS - e \int_{S_l} j_n^+ \, dS$$

where S_l is the lateral boundary of the sensitive volume and S^+ is the boundary at the positive electrode.

For j^+ and j^- substitute the expressions given by Eq. 17. Since n^+ and n^- are zero at S^+ and S^-, and w_n is zero at S_l, then

$$I = e \int_A n_0 \, dA - e \int_A \beta n^+ n^- \, dA + e \int_{S^-} D^- \, (grad \, n^-)_n \, dS$$

$$+ e \int_{S^+} D^+ \, (grad \, n^+)_n \, dS + e \int_{S_l} D^+ \, (grad \, n^+)_n \, dS \tag{20}$$

The physical interpretation of Eq. 20 is quite simple. The number of positive charges entering the collecting (negative) electrode is equal to the number of positive ions formed in the active volume (first term), minus the number of positive ions that recombine (second term), minus the number of positive ions that diffuse back to the positive electrode (fourth term, always negative), minus or plus the number of positive ions that diffuse out of or into the sensitive volume through its lateral boundary (fifth term). To obtain the current in the measuring instrument from the number of positive charges entering the collecting electrode, subtract the number of negative charges that diffuse back to this electrode (third term, always negative). The term $e \int_A n_0 \, dA$, which represents the saturation current, is independent of the voltage applied, except in so far as the lateral boundary of the sensitive volume is modified by the field produced by the space charge. The other terms decrease with increasing voltage.

As an example, consider a parallel plate chamber of depth d uniformly irradiated over its active volume and beyond it for a large distance from the edge of the collecting electrode.

We may assume first that recombination is negligible. As in Sec. 2.2, a cartesian coordinate system may be used, with its origin on the positive electrode and its x axis in the direction of the electric field. Again w^+ and w^- denote the absolute values of the drift velocities; j^+ and j^- are absolute values of the current vectors. Equation 17 becomes

$$j^+ = n^+ w^+ - D^+ \frac{dn^+}{dx}$$

$$j^- = n^- w^- + D^- \frac{dn^-}{dx} \tag{21}$$

while Eq. 18 gives

$$\frac{dj^+}{dx} = -\frac{dj^-}{dx} = n_0 = \text{const.} \tag{22}$$

Integration of Eq. 22, substitution in Eq. 21, and integration of the resulting equations yield

$$n^+ = \frac{n_0}{w^+} x + h^+ e^{w^+ x / D^+} + k^+$$

$$n^- = -\frac{n_0}{w^-} x + h^- e^{w^- x / D^-} + k^- \tag{23}$$

where h^+, h^-, k^+, and k^- are constants to be determined with the boundary conditions

$$n^+ = n^- = 0 \quad \text{at } x = 0 \text{ and } x = d$$

With these conditions

$$n^+ = \frac{n_0}{w^+} x - \frac{n_0}{w^+} d \frac{e^{w^+ x / D^+} - 1}{e^{w^+ d / D^+} - 1}$$

$$n^- = -\frac{n_0}{w^-} x + \frac{n_0}{w^-} d \frac{1 - e^{-w^- x / D^-}}{1 - e^{-w^- d / D^-}} \tag{24}$$

According to Eq. 18, Chap. 1, the following relation holds:

$$\frac{wd}{D} = \frac{eEd}{\epsilon kT} = \frac{V_0}{2.5 \times 10^{-2}} \frac{1}{\epsilon} \tag{25}$$

where $V_0 = Ed$ is the voltage difference between the electrodes. In most practical cases w^+d/D^+ and w^-d/D^- are large numbers so that Eq. 24 can be simplified as follows:

$$n^+ = \frac{n_0}{w^+} x - \frac{n_0}{w^+} de^{-w^+(d-x)/D^+}$$

$$n^- = \frac{n_0}{w^-} (d - x) - \frac{n_0}{w^-} de^{-w^-x/D^-} \tag{24a}$$

Comparison between Eq. 15 or 16 and Eq. 24a shows that diffusion has an appreciable effect on the distribution of positive and negative ions only in the neighborhood of the negative or positive electrode, respectively.

Equations 21 and 24 yield

$$j^+ = n_0 x + \frac{n_0 d}{e^{w^+ d/D^+} - 1} - \frac{n_0}{w^+} D^+$$

$$j^- = -n_0 x + \frac{n_0 d}{1 - e^{-w^- d/D^-}} - \frac{n_0}{w^-} D^- \tag{26}$$

or, when $w^+ d/D^+$ and $w^- d/D^-$ are large numbers,

$$j^+ = n_0 x - \frac{n_0}{w^+} D^+$$

$$j^- = n_0(d - x) - \frac{n_0}{w^-} D^- \tag{26a}$$

The current I through a section of the sensitive volume at the distance x from the positive electrode has the value

$$I = eS(j^+ + j^-)$$

where S is the area of the collecting electrode, or using Eq. 26a

$$I = eS \, dn_0 - eS \left(\frac{n_0}{w^+} D^+ + \frac{n_0}{w^-} D^- \right) \qquad (27)$$

This expression is independent of x because, under the assumption that the ionization extends with uniform density some distance beyond the lateral boundary of the sensitive volume, the net effect of the diffusion across this boundary is zero.

Equation 27 shows that the lack of saturation caused by diffusion has the fractional value

$$\left(-\frac{\delta I}{I} \right)_{\text{diff.}} = \frac{D^+}{w^+ d} + \frac{D^-}{w^- d} = \frac{2.5 \times 10^{-2}}{V_0} \left(\epsilon^+ + \epsilon^- \right) \qquad (28)$$

The agitation energy ϵ is practically 1 for ions, while it may be of the order of several hundred for electrons. Hence, when the negative carriers are electrons, the effect of diffusion may become appreciable for values of V_0 of a few hundred volts. If, however, the negative carriers are ions, the effect of diffusion becomes appreciable only at much lower values of V_0.

In order to evaluate the influence of recombination on the ionization current in a parallel plate chamber, we assume that both diffusion and recombination have a very small effect on the distribution of positive and negative ions in the chamber. This assumption, as far as diffusion is concerned, is justified by the preceding results. Using for n^+ and n^- the expressions in Eq. 16, Eq. 20 yields the following for the lack of saturation caused by recombination:

$$\left(-\frac{\delta I}{I} \right)_{\text{recomb.}} = \frac{\beta}{n_0 d} \int_0^d n^+ n^- \, dx \qquad (29)$$

or

$$\left(-\frac{\delta I}{I} \right)_{\text{recomb.}} = \frac{\beta}{6} \frac{n_0 d^2}{w^+ w^-}$$

When the negative carriers are free electrons the recombination constant β is about 10^4 times smaller and the drift velocity w^- about 10^3 times larger than when the negative carriers are heavy ions. Thus the recombination is usually negligible in gases in which the electrons remain free, but it may become important in gases in which electron attachment takes place. This does not necessarily apply to columnar recombination, which may be appreciable even in the case of free electrons.

When the negative carriers are ions, we may take $\beta = 2 \times 10^{-6}$ and $w^+ = w^- = 1.3E$. For $d = 1$ cm the recombination correction thus becomes $2 \times 10^{-7}(n_0/V_0^2)$. With an intensity of ionization of 1 roentgen /sec, $n_0 \approx 2 \times 10^9$ and $V_0 = 100$ volts, the correction is about 4 per cent. The correction is enormously smaller when the negative carriers are free electrons.

Chapter 3

OPERATION OF IONIZATION CHAMBERS WITH VARIABLE IONIZATION

3.1 <u>General Considerations</u>. The results in the preceding chapter were obtained for a source of ionization constant in time. But they are also valid when the intensity of the source varies with time, provided the variations are sufficiently slow. By this it is meant that no appreciable change of intensity takes place within a time of the order of the transit time of the positive ions through the chamber. This time is usually of the order of milliseconds.

Now consider the case of a rapidly varying ionization that includes, as a limit, the case of a large number of ion pairs being produced simultaneously in the chamber by an ionizing particle such as, for example, an α particle. To calculate the current in the external circuit as a function of time, it is necessary to consider separately the charges induced on the collecting electrode by the motion of the various types of charged particles present in the gas. For the sake of simplicity and because it occurs most frequently, let us assume that no attachment takes place. Thus the negative carriers are free electrons. Recombination and diffusion will be neglected. Furthermore we shall assume, for the time being, that the main part of the ionization is produced sufficiently far from the guard electrode that the charge induced on that electrode by the motion of the ions and electrons can be disregarded. The "edge effects," i.e., the phenomena observed when the charged particles move in the neighborhood of the boundary of the sensitive volume, will be discussed separately in Sec. 3.7.

With the above assumptions, the effects of the motion of charged particles between the electrodes of an ionization chamber can be calculated most easily and generally by applying the principle of conservation of energy.

Consider first an ionization chamber connected to a voltage supply through a current meter, as in Fig. 3.1. Assume that the resistance

31

of the external circuit is negligible, so that the collecting electrode will be permanently at zero voltage and the high-voltage electrode will be at the constant voltage V_0. If ions and electrons are present

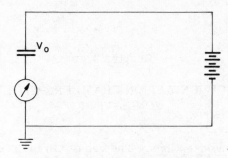

Fig. 3.1 — Connection diagram of an ionization chamber.

in the gas of the chamber, the electric field in the chamber may be regarded as the superposition of two fields — one produced by the voltage difference between the electrodes and described by the field strength $\vec{E}$ and potential V, the other produced by the space charge $\rho = e(n^+ - n^-)$ and described by the field strength $\vec{E}_\rho$ and the potential V_ρ. The corresponding quantities for the actual field will be $\vec{E} + \vec{E}_\rho$, $V + V_\rho$.

The voltage V satisfies the equation

$$\nabla^2 V = 0 \tag{1}$$

and the boundary conditions

$$V = 0 \text{ at the collecting electrode}$$
$$V = V_0 \text{ at the high-voltage electrode} \tag{2}$$

The voltage V_ρ satisfies the equation

$$\nabla^2 V_\rho = -4\pi\rho = -4\pi e(n^+ - n^-) \tag{3}$$

and the boundary conditions

$$V_\rho = 0 \text{ at both electrodes} \tag{4}$$

The electrostatic energy of the field is

$$\frac{1}{8\pi} \int_A (\vec{E} + \vec{E}_p)^2 \, dA = \frac{1}{8\pi} \int_A E^2 \, dA + \frac{1}{8\pi} \int_A E_p^2 \, dA + \frac{1}{4\pi} \int_A \vec{E} \cdot \vec{E}_p \, dA$$

where A is the sensitive volume of the chamber.

The third integral on the right-hand side can be transformed

$$\int_A \vec{E} \cdot \vec{E}_p \, dA = - \int_A \vec{E} \cdot \text{grad } V_p \, dA$$

$$= - \int_A \text{div } (V_p \vec{E}) \, dA + \int_A V_p \, \text{div } \vec{E} \, dA$$

$$= \int_A V_p \, \text{div } \vec{E} \, dA - \int_S V_p E_n \, dS$$

where S is the combined surface of the two electrodes and E_n is the component of $\vec{E}$ perpendicular to S. ($\vec{E}_p$ and V_p are assumed to be zero at the lateral boundary of the sensitive volume.) Now div $\vec{E}$ = $-\nabla^2 V = 0$ while $V_p = 0$ at the surface S. Hence, $\int \vec{E} \cdot \vec{E}_p \, dA = 0$ and, if W and W_p are the electrostatic energies of the fields represented by $\vec{E}$ and $\vec{E}_p$, respectively, the total electrostatic energy is given by

$$\frac{1}{8\pi} \int_A (\vec{E} + \vec{E}_p)^2 \, dA = W + W_p \qquad (5)$$

Electrons and ions in the ionized gas move along the lines of force with a comparatively small velocity that is constant except in so far as the electric field strength varies from point to point. Hence, variations in the kinetic energy of electrons and ions are wholly negligible and practically all the work performed by the electric field on the charged particles during their motion is used up to overcome the "frictional forces" represented by collisions with gas molecules. The principle of conservation of energy can then be expressed as in Eq. 6; i.e., the work of the electric field plus the variation of the electrostatic energy is equal to the work performed by the voltage supply. Since W is constant in time

$$e \int_A (\vec{E} + \vec{E}_p) \cdot (n^+ \vec{w}^+ - n^- \vec{w}^-) \, dA + \frac{dW_p}{dt} = V_0 I \qquad (6)$$

where I is the current in the external circuit and n^+, n^-, $\vec{w}^+$, and $\vec{w}^-$ are, as before, the densities and the drift velocities of positive ions and electrons, respectively.

Since $V_\rho = 0$ at the surface S which bounds the volume A, the two following equations hold

$$\int_A \text{div}\,[V_\rho(n^+\vec{w}^+ - n^-\vec{w}^-)]\;dA = 0$$

$$\int_A \text{div}\left(V_\rho\,\frac{\partial \vec{E}_\rho}{\partial t}\right)dA = 0$$

from which it follows

$$\int_A \vec{E}_\rho \cdot (n^+\vec{w}^+ - n^-\vec{w}^-)\;dA = \int_A V_\rho\,\text{div}\,(n^+\vec{w}^+ - n^-\vec{w}^-)\;dA$$

$$\int_A \vec{E}_\rho \cdot \frac{\partial \vec{E}_\rho}{\partial t}\;dA = \int_A V_\rho\,\text{div}\,\frac{\partial \vec{E}_\rho}{\partial t}\;dA$$

$$= 4\,\pi\int_A V_\rho\,\frac{\partial \rho}{\partial t}\;dA$$

On the other hand,

$$\frac{1}{4\pi}\int_A \vec{E}_\rho\,\frac{\partial \vec{E}_\rho}{\partial t}\;dA = \frac{\partial W_\rho}{\partial t}$$

$$\frac{\partial \rho}{\partial t} = -\,\text{div}\,e(n^+\vec{w}^+ - n^-\vec{w}^-)$$

so that, from the two equations above,

$$e\int_A \vec{E}_\rho \cdot (n^+\vec{w}^+ - n^-\vec{w}^-)\;dA + \frac{\partial W_\rho}{\partial t} = 0 \tag{7}$$

Subtracting Eq. 7 from Eq. 6 gives for the external current I in terms of the motion of the electrons and ions in the chamber

$$I = \frac{e}{V_0}\int_A \vec{E} \cdot (n^+\vec{w}^+ - n^-\vec{w}^-)\;dA \tag{8}$$

This may be written

$$I = I^+ + I^-$$

using the notations

$$I^+ = \frac{e}{V_0} \int_A n^+ \vec{E} \cdot \vec{w}^+ \, dA$$

$$I^- = -\frac{e}{V_0} \int_A n^- \vec{E} \cdot \vec{w}^- \, dA$$

(9)

or

$$I^+ = \frac{e}{V_0} \sum \vec{E_i}^+ \cdot \vec{w_i}^+$$

$$I^- = -\frac{e}{V_0} \sum \vec{E_i}^- \cdot \vec{w_i}^-$$

(9a)

where $\vec{w_i}^+$ and $\vec{w_i}^-$ represent the drift velocities of the ith ion or electron at the moment under consideration, and where $\vec{E_i}^+$ and $\vec{E_i}^-$ are the electric field strengths at the place where these particles are located. The summations are extended to all ions and electrons present in the chamber. I^+ and I^- represent the currents induced by the motion of the positive ions and of the electrons, respectively. They will be denoted briefly as "positive ion current" and "electron current." In computing these currents, the values of the field to be taken into consideration are those that exist in the chamber when no space charge is present. The vectors $\vec{E}/V_0$ depend only on the geometrical configuration of the chamber and are independent of the value V_0 for the applied voltage.

The following notations will also be used:

$$Q^+(t) = \int_0^t I^+(t) \, dt$$

$$Q^-(t) = \int_0^t I^-(t) \, dt$$

(10)

The quantities Q^+ and Q^- may be regarded as the charges induced by the motion of the positive ions and electrons, respectively, on the collecting electrode in the time interval between 0 and t.

Ordinarily for the measurement of variable ionization currents the collecting electrode is connected to ground through a leak resistor R. The voltage V developed across this resistor by the ionization current is fed to the input of an electronic amplifier (see Fig. 3.2). Application of the energy principle to this case, under the assumption that

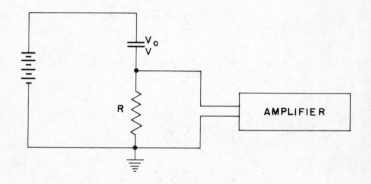

Fig. 3.2 — Connection diagram of an ionization chamber.

$V \ll V_0$, yields for V

$$V + RC \frac{dV}{dt} = RI(t) \tag{11}$$

where I is given by Eq. 8 and C is the total capacity of the collecting electrode and of the amplifier input. If the product RC is very small, the second term on the left-hand side can be neglected and Eq. 11 reduces to

$$V(t) = RI(t) \tag{12}$$

If RC is very large, the first term can be neglected and Eq. 11 yields

$$V(t) - V(0) = \frac{Q(t)}{C} \tag{13}$$

where $Q = Q^+ + Q^-$ and where Q^+ and Q^- are given by Eq. 10. In the general case, Eq. 11 has the solution

$$V(t) - V(0) = e^{-t/RC} \frac{1}{C} \int_0^t e^{t_1/RC} I(t_1) \, dt_1 \tag{14}$$

3.2 <u>Ionization Pulse</u>. Suppose that N_0 ion pairs are simultaneously produced in the chamber at the time $t = 0$, as by an α particle.
If the effect of the space charge on the drift velocities is neglected,
$\vec{w}^+$ and $\vec{w}^-$ are known functions of the position, and it is possible, at
least in principle, to determine the motion of each positive ion and
each electron. Once this is done, $I^+(t)$ and $I^-(t)$ can be calculated as
functions of time by Eq. 9. Integrating with respect to time gives the
expression for $Q^+(t)$ and $Q^-(t)$

$$Q^+(t) = \frac{e}{V_0} \sum_1^{N_0} [V_i(0) - V_i^+(t)]$$

$$Q^-(t) = -\frac{e}{V_0} \sum_1^{N_0} [V_i(0) - V_i^-(t)]$$

(15)

In the above equations $V_i(0)$ represents the potential at the point
where the ith ion pair is formed, $V_i^+(t)$ represents the potential at
the point where the ith positive ion is located at the time t, and $V_i^-(t)$
has a similar meaning for the ith electron. The electrons have large
drift velocities; hence Q^- varies very rapidly with time until all the
electrons have reached the positive electrode. From that time on Q^-
has the constant value

$$Q_0^- = -\frac{e}{V_0} \sum_1^{N_0} [V_i(0) - V^+]$$

(16)

where V^+ is the voltage of the positive electrode. The positive ions
have much smaller drift velocities. Hence $Q^+(t)$ reaches its final
value after a much longer time. This value is given by

$$Q_0^+ = \frac{e}{V_0} \sum_1^{N_0} [V_i(0) - V^-]$$

(17)

where V^- is the voltage of the negative electrode.

The sum of Q_0^- and Q_0^+ is, of course, equal to $N_0 e$, as can be shown
by adding Eqs. 16 and 17 since $V^+ - V^- = V_0$.

Suppose now that the leak resistor R is chosen so as to make the
time constant RC large compared with the time of collection of the
positive ions. Then, according to Eq. 13, the voltage V of the collect-

ing electrode (assumed to be zero at t = 0) is proportional to $Q(t) = Q^-(t) + Q^+(t)$. Therefore it increases very rapidly at first until all electrons have been collected, then very slowly until the positive ions have also been collected. When both electrons and positive ions have been swept from the chamber the voltage of the collecting electrode becomes

$$V_P = \frac{Q_0^- + Q_0^+}{C} = \frac{N_0 e}{C} \tag{18}$$

Subsequently, it decays exponentially with the time constant RC.

A chamber operated under the conditions specified above will be called an ion-pulse chamber. The advantage of an ion-pulse chamber is that the pulse height V_P is proportional to the total number N_0 of ions produced in the chamber, irrespective of the position where they are produced. The main disadvantage is that the time for collection of the positive ions is usually of the order of milliseconds, so that the decay constant RC must be of at least the order of 0.01 sec and the amplifier must have its low-frequency cutoff at a correspondingly small frequency (see Sec. 3.3). This makes the arrangement unsuitable for fast counting and very sensitive to microphonic disturbances and to a-c pickup.

For these reasons, the value of the resistance R is often chosen so that RC is large compared with the time for collection of the electrons but small compared with the time for collection of the positive ions. Since a chamber operated under these conditions responds only to the fast part of the pulse, i.e., to that part of the pulse due to the motion of the electrons, it will be called an electron-pulse chamber. The time for collection of electrons is ordinarily of the order of 1 μsec, so time constant RC need not be larger than 10 or 20 μsec. Thus the chamber will be able to record pulses following one another at very short time intervals, and the arrangement will be insensitive to microphonics or to a-c disturbances.

The disadvantage of an electron-pulse chamber is that the pulse height will depend not only on the total number N_0 of ion pairs produced in the chamber, but also on the position where they are produced. The pulse height can be computed to a very good approximation (i.e., neglecting terms of the order of w^+/w^-) by considering the effect of the motion of the electrons and neglecting altogether the effect of the motion of positive ions. Since RC is assumed to be large compared with the time for collection of the electrons, the value of the pulse height will be given by

$$V_P = \frac{Q_o^-}{C} \tag{19}$$

There is a simple device by which the size of pulses in an electron-pulse chamber may be made independent of the position where the ionization is produced. This device consists of a grid placed between the two electrodes and held at an appropriate intermediate voltage. Suppose that the collecting electrode is positive and that the ionization is produced between the grid and the negative electrode. The grid shields the collecting electrode from the effects of the motion of charged particles as long as they are between the grid and the high-voltage electrode. The positive ions never penetrate the region between the grid and the collecting electrode. The electrons, however, will penetrate this region, except for the few that may be captured by the grid wires. While traveling between the grid and the collecting electrode, each electron will induce on this electrode a charge equal to its own. Therefore the total charge induced on the collecting electrode by the motion of the electrons will be proportional to the number of ion pairs produced in the chamber. No charge will be induced by the motion of the positive ions. A practical application of this principle will be described in Chap. 6, Sec. 6.1.

3.3 <u>Influence on the Pulse Shape of the Transient Response of the Amplifier; Measure of Pulse Heights in Mev.</u> We have considered so far the voltage pulse produced by the ionization current at the amplifier input. To determine the observed voltage pulse at the output of the amplifier, the transient response of the amplifier must be taken into account. In order to define the transient response of the amplifier, suppose that a charge, Q, is brought onto the collecting electrode at the time t = 0. This can be done by applying at t = 0 a square voltage wave to the high-voltage electrode of the chamber. The voltage V of the collector rises abruptly to a value equal to Q/C and then decays exponentially with a time constant RC, as indicated by curve a in Fig. 3.3. Curve b in the same figure represents the voltage $V_e(t)$ at the output of the amplifier as a function of time. The function $\psi(t) = V(t)/Q$, which if the amplifier is linear is independent of Q, is defined as the transient response of the amplifier (see also Chap. 3 of "Electronics: Experimental Techniques," by W.C. Elmore and M. L. Sands).

The output voltage in terms of the ionization current I and of the transient response ψ is

$$V_e\ (t) = \int_0^\infty I(t - t_1)\ \psi(t_1)\ dt_1 \tag{20}$$

which can be considered as a generalization of Eq. 14. The function $\psi(t)$ depends on the characteristics of the input circuit (capacity C, resistance R) as well as on those of the amplifier. It reduces to the exponential function, exp $(-t/RC)$, if the amplifier has infinite bandwidth.

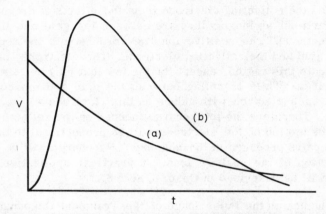

Fig. 3.3 — Transient response of an amplifier. (a) Input voltage. (b) Output voltage.

The area under the curve $\psi(t)$ divided by its maximum ordinate may be defined as the "resolving time" of the amplifier. For an exponential response of the type represented by curve a, the resolving time is equal to RC.

Another term frequently used in connection with the transient response of an amplifier is the "rise time." It is difficult to give a precise definition for rise time, which applies to an arbitrary transient response. We may take it to be the time during which the voltage pulse increases from 10 per cent to 90 per cent of its maximum value.

It is convenient to define the transient response of an ionization chamber, f(t), by

$$I(t) = N_0 e\ f(t) \tag{21}$$

where $I(t)$ represents the current at the time t under the assumption that N_0 ion pairs are produced at the time $t = 0$. It should be pointed out that $f(t)$ depends not only on the properties of the ion chamber, but also on the space distribution of the ionization.

The function $f(t)$ may be split into the sum of two functions $f^+(t)$ and $f^-(t)$ relative to the positive ion current and to the electron current, respectively, which are defined as

$$I^+(t) = N_0 e \, f^+(t)$$
$$I^-(t) = N_0 e \, f^-(t)$$

(21a)

Comparison with Eqs. 9 and 9a gives for $f^+(t)$ and $f^-(t)$ the equations

$$f^+(t) = \frac{1}{N_0 V_0} \int_A n^+(t) \vec{E} \cdot \vec{w}^+ \cdot dA = \frac{1}{N_0 V_0} \sum_1^{N_0} \vec{E}_i^+ \cdot \vec{w}_i^+$$

$$f^-(t) = -\frac{1}{N_0 V_0} \int_A n^-(t) \vec{E} \cdot \vec{w}^- \cdot dA = -\frac{1}{N_0 V_0} \sum_1^{N_0} \vec{E}_i^- \cdot \vec{w}_i^-$$

(22)

Notice that $f^+(t)$ and $f^-(t)$ may be considered as the averages, over all the positive ions and all the electrons, respectively, of the quantities $\vec{w}^+ \cdot (\vec{E}/V_0)$ and $-\vec{w}^- \cdot (\vec{E}/V_0)$ at the time t after the ionization pulse. In computing these averages a particle that has been collected is considered as still existing but having zero velocity.

The transient response $X(t)$ of the detecting equipment, consisting of an ionization chamber and an amplifier, may be defined by the equation

$$V_e(t) = N_0 e \, X(t)$$

(23)

where $V_e(t)$ represents the output voltage as a function of time in the case that N_0 ion pairs are produced in the chamber at $t = 0$. From Eqs. 20, 21, and 23 and the fact that $f(t) = 0$ for $t < 0$, is derived the relation

$$X(t) = \int_0^t f(t - t_1) \, \psi(t_1) \, dt_1$$

(24)

By using the resolving time of the amplifier in place of the time constant RC, the conditions stated in Sec. 3.2 for the operation of a chamber as an ion-pulse or an electron-pulse chamber may be generalized to include the influence of the amplifier on the observed pulse shape. A chamber is an ion-pulse chamber if the resolving time of the amplifier is long compared with the time of collection of the positive ions; it is an electron-pulse chamber if the resolving time is short compared with the time of collection of positive ions but long compared with the time of collection of electrons. A convenient measure for the size of ionization pulses is the quantity $P = (Q/e)W_0$, where Q is the charge induced on the collecting electrode ($Q = Q_0^+ + Q_0^- = N_0e$ for an ion-pulse chamber; $Q = Q_0^-$ for an electron-pulse chamber) and W_0 is the energy for the formation of an ion pair in electron volts (see the appendix, Sec. 2). P is thus expressed in electron volts and, in the case of an ion-pulse chamber, simply represents the energy N_0W_0 dissipated in the chamber by the ionizing particle that produces the pulse. In the case of an electron-pulse chamber, P represents a fraction of this energy, given by

$$P = N_0 W_0 \frac{Q_0^-}{Q_0^+ + Q_0^-}$$

For an absolute calibration of a chamber operated in conjunction with an amplifier and a recording device, the most direct procedure consists in observing the pulses from a source of α particles of uniform and known energy, usually a polonium source, placed in the chamber in such a way that the whole range of the α particle is within the sensitive volume. If the chamber is operated as an ion-pulse chamber, the output pulses all have the same size, and this size corresponds to ionization pulses of magnitude P equal to the energy of the α particles. If the chamber is operated as an electron-pulse chamber the output pulses will generally have different sizes. To obtain the relation between the response of the measuring instrument and the value P of the corresponding ionization pulse, compute theoretically the distribution in size of the ionization pulses and then fit the computed curve to the experimental pulse-height distribution (see Chap. 6, Sec. 6.1).

A more convenient but less direct method of calibration consists in feeding known voltage pulses, V_1, to the high-voltage electrode of the ionization chamber and observing the corresponding output pulses. If C_1 is the partial capacity of the collecting electrode with respect to the high-voltage electrode and C is the total capacity of the collecting electrode and the amplifier input, a voltage pulse V_1 at the high-voltage electrode produces a pulse $V_P = V_1 C_1/C$ at the input of the amplifier. The P value of this pulse is given by $(V_1 C_1/e)W_0$, by definition. In other words, the signal obtained by applying a voltage pulse V_1 to the high-voltage electrode of the ionization chamber is equal to the signal produced by an ionizing particle that liberates a charge $Q = V_1 C_1$ in the chamber, provided that the chamber is operated for ion pulses.

It will be noted that the method outlined requires knowledge of W_0 and of the partial capacity C_1 of the collecting electrode with respect to the high-voltage electrode, which can usually be computed quite accurately. It does not require knowledge of the stray capacity, which could, in general, be determined only by direct measurement.

3.4 <u>Continuously Variable Ionization</u>. Suppose now that the ionization chamber is irradiated with a continuous source of ionization of variable intensity, so that a total of $N(t)\,dt$ ion pairs are produced within its sensitive volume in the time interval between t and $t + dt$. If the currents $I^+(t)$ and $I^-(t)$ have been determined for an instantaneous ionization pulse, they can also be calculated for continuously variable ionization in the same chamber for the same spatial distribution of ionization. This is true because a continuous ionization can always be subdivided, ideally, into an infinite number of infinitely short ionization pulses. By making use of the functions $f^+(t)$ and $f^-(t)$ defined by Eqs. 21a, we obtain for $I^+(t)$ and $I^-(t)$ the following expressions:

$$I^+(t) = e \int_0^\infty N(t - t_1) f^+(t_1)\,dt_1$$
$$I^-(t) = e \int_0^\infty N(t - t_1) f^-(t_1)\,dt_1 \qquad (25)$$

In particular, if N is constant, I^+ and I^- become

$$I_0^+ = eN \int_0^\infty f^+(t_1)\,dt_1$$
$$I_0^- = eN \int_0^\infty f^-(t_1)\,dt_1 \qquad (25a)$$

Equations 25a acquire a simple physical meaning if one considers that, according to Eqs. 22,

$$\int_0^\infty f^+(t)\,dt = \frac{1}{N_0 V_0} \sum_1^{N_0} \int_0^\infty \vec{E}_i \cdot \vec{w}_i\,dt$$

$$= \frac{1}{N_0 V_0} \sum_1^{N_0} [V_i\,(0) - V^-]$$

$$= \frac{1}{V_0} [V_i\,(0) - V^-]_{av}$$

and similarly

$$\int_0^\infty f^-(t) \, dt = \frac{1}{V_0} [V^+ - V_i(0)]_{av}$$

where $[V_i(0) - V^-]_{av}$ and $[V^+ - V_i(0)]_{av}$ represent the average values of the difference of potential between the place of production of the ions and the negative or positive electrode, respectively (see Sec. 3.2). Hence Eq. 25a yields

$$I_0^+ = e \, \frac{N}{V_0} \, [V_i(0) - V^-]_{av}$$

$$(25b)$$

$$I_0^- = e \, \frac{N}{V_0} \, [V^+ - V_i(0)]_{av}$$

It follows from Eq. 25b that the total ionization current is

$$I_0 = I_0^+ + I_0^- = eN$$

in agreement with Eq. 5 in Chap. 2. The output voltage $V_e(t)$ is given by the equation

$$V_e(t) = e \int_0^\infty N(t - t_1) \, X(t_1) \, dt_1 \qquad (26)$$

which may be considered as a direct consequence of Eq. 23, or can be derived from Eqs. 20, 24, and 25 by taking into account that $\psi(t) = 0$ for $t < 0$.

If the source of ionization is suddenly turned on to a constant value at the time $t = 0$ [$N(t) = 0$ for $t < 0$; $N(t) = N = $ const. for $t > 0$] I^+ and I^- are zero for $t < 0$ and have the following expressions for $t > 0$:

$$I^+(t) = eN \int_0^t f^+(t_1) \, dt_1$$

$$(27)$$

$$I^-(t) = eN \int_0^t f^-(t_1) \, dt_1$$

If a constant source of ionization is suddenly turned off at $t = 0$ [$N(t) = N = $ const. for $t < 0$; $N(t) = 0$ for $t > 0$] the expressions are,

$$\left. \begin{array}{l} I^+(t) = I_0^+ \\ I^-(t) = I_0^- \end{array} \right\} \quad \text{for } t <$$

$$I^+(t) = I_0^+ \left[1 - \frac{eN}{I_0^+} \int_0^t f^+(t_1) \, dt_1 \right] \Bigg]$$

$$\text{for } t > 0$$

$$I^-(t) = I_0^- \left[1 - \frac{eN}{I_0^-} \int_0^t f^-(t_1) \, dt_1 \right] \Bigg]$$

$$(28)$$

The expressions for the charges $Q^+(t)$ and $Q^-(t)$ for the case of an instantaneous ionization pulse (see Eq. 10) can be written in terms of $f^+(t)$ and $f^-(t)$ as

$$Q^+(t) = N_0 e \int_0^t f^+(t_1) \, dt_1$$

$$Q^-(t) = N_0 e \int_0^t f^-(t_1) \, dt_1$$

$$(29)$$

Comparison with Eqs. 27 and 28 shows that the positive ion current and the electron current present in a chamber after a constant source of ionization is suddenly turned on or off exhibit the same time dependence as the charges induced on the collecting electrode by the motion of the positive ions and the electrons, respectively, after an infinitely short ionization pulse.

In general, the variations of the ionization current will be proportional to the variations of the source intensity only if the latter variations are (1) very slow compared with the time for collection of positive ions, or (2) very fast compared with the time for collection of positive ions, but very slow compared with the time for collection of electrons. In the first instance the total ionization current $I^+ + I^-$ will follow the variations of intensity in the ionizing radiation. In the second instance, the electron current I^- will follow the changes of the ionizing radiation, but the positive ion current I^+ will remain practically constant. The exact value of the ionization current $I(t) = I^+(t) + I^-(t)$ produced by a given variable source of ionization may be computed by means of Eq. 25, if the function $f(t) = f^+(t) + f^-(t)$ is known. This function can be determined by observing the variations of I immediately after a constant source of ionization has been turned on or off.

3.5 Parallel-plate Chamber. In a parallel-plate chamber the electric field is constant if space-charge effects can be neglected; hence the drift velocities of both positive ions and electrons are independent of position. It follows that $I^+(t)$ and $I^-(t)$ are proportional to the numbers of positive ions and of electrons, respectively, present in the chamber at the time t.

The potential difference between two points of the chamber is proportional to the difference of their distances from the negative electrode. Therefore, the expressions for $Q^+(t)$ and $Q^-(t)$ in the case of an instantaneous ionization pulse (see Eq. 15) become

$$Q^+(t) = \frac{e}{h} \sum_1^{N_0} [\, x_i(0) - x_i^+(t)\,]$$

$$Q^-(t) = -\frac{e}{h} \sum_1^{N_0} [\, x_i(0) - x_i^-(t)\,]$$

(30)

where h is the separation of the electrodes, $x_i(0)$ is the distance from the negative electrode to the point where the ith ion pair is formed, $x_i^+(t)$ and $x_i^-(t)$ are the distances from the negative electrode to the ith positive ion and the ith electron, respectively, at the time t after the ionization pulse. From Eq. 30 it follows that the charges Q_0^- and Q_0^+ induced by the motion of the electrons and of the positive ions after complete collection are given by $N_0 e/h$ times the distance of the center of gravity of the ionization from the positive and negative electrodes, respectively. It follows from Eq. 25b that, if the chamber is irradiated by a constant source of ionization so that N ion pairs are produced per unit time, the electron and positive ion currents I_0^- and I_0^+ are given by the product of eN/h times the distance of the center of gravity of the ionization from the positive and negative electrodes, respectively. If, for instance, the volume of the chamber is uniformly irradiated, the center of gravity of the ionization is halfway between the positive and negative electrodes. The currents I_0^+ and I_0^- are then identical and given by

$$I_0^+ = I_0^- = \tfrac{1}{2} eN$$

In this case of spatially uniform ionization, the functions $f^-(t)$ and $f^+(t)$ have the expressions

$$f^+(t) = \frac{h - w^+ t}{h^2}\, w^+ \qquad \text{for } t < h/w^+$$

$$f^+(t) = 0 \qquad \text{for } t > h/w^+$$

$$f^-(t) = \frac{h - w^- t}{h^2}\, w^- \qquad \text{for } t < h/w^-$$

$$f^-(t) = 0 \qquad \text{for } t > h/w^-$$

(31)

The expressions for the positive ion and electron currents subsequent to a sudden turning on of a constant source of ionization (see Eq. 27) become

$$I^+(t) = e \frac{Nw^+}{h} \left(t - \frac{1}{2} \frac{w^+}{h} t^2 \right) \qquad \text{for } t < h/w^+$$

$$I^+(t) = \frac{1}{2} eN = I_0^+ \qquad \text{for } t > h/w^+$$

$$I^-(t) = e \frac{Nw^-}{h} \left(t - \frac{1}{2} \frac{w^-}{h} t^2 \right) \qquad \text{for } t < h/w^-$$

$$I^-(t) = \frac{1}{2} eN = I_0^- \qquad \text{for } t > h/w^-$$

(32)

Similarly, in the case of a sudden stoppage of the source (see Eq. 28)

$$I^+(t) = eN \left[\frac{1}{2} - \frac{w^+}{h} t + \frac{1}{2} \left(\frac{w^+}{h} t \right)^2 \right] \qquad \text{for } t < h/w^+$$

$$I^+(t) = 0 \qquad \text{for } t > h/w^-$$

$$I^-(t) = eN \left[\frac{1}{2} - \frac{w^-}{h} t + \frac{1}{2} \left(\frac{w^-}{h} t \right)^2 \right] \qquad \text{for } t < h/w^-$$

$$I^-(t) = 0 \qquad \text{for } t > h/w^-$$

(33)

3.6 Cadlindrical Chamber. Consider first the case of N_0 ion pairs formed instantaneously at a distance r from the axis of the chamber, as by an α particle traveling parallel to the axis. Suppose that the outer electrode is negative and the inner electrode positive. After all electrons and ions have been collected, the charges Q_0^+ and Q_0^- induced by the motion of the positive ions and the electrons, respectively, are given by the expressions (see Eqs. 16 and 17):

$$Q_0^+ = eN_0 \frac{\ln (b/r)}{\ln (b/a)}$$

$$Q_0^- = eN_0 \frac{\ln (r/a)}{\ln (b/a)}$$

(34)

where a is the radius of the inner and b that of the outer cylinder.

In Fig. 3.4, Q_0^+ and Q_0^- are plotted as functions of r/a for b = 100a. Notice that, when $b \gg a$, as assumed here, Q_0^- is much larger than Q_0^+, except when the ions are formed very close to the central electrode.

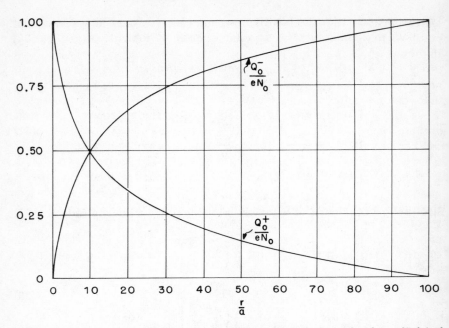

Fig. 3.4—Charges Q_0^+ and Q_0^- induced on the collecting electrode of a cylindrical chamber by the motion of positive ions and electrons, respectively, when N_0 ion pairs are formed at a distance r from the axis. Inner electrode positive; b = 100a (b = radius of the outer electrode; a = radius of the inner electrode).

In the case of a cylindrical chamber uniformly irradiated by a constant source of ionization producing N ion pairs per unit time, Eq. 25b gives for the positive ion and electron currents

$$\frac{I_0^+}{eN} = \frac{1}{2 \ln (b/a)} - \frac{a^2}{b^2 - a^2}$$

$$\frac{I_0^-}{eN} = \frac{b^2}{b^2 - a^2} - \frac{1}{2 \ln (b/a)}$$

(35)

or, if $b \gg a$,

$$\frac{I_0^+}{eN} = \frac{1}{2 \ln (b/a)}$$

$$\frac{I_0^-}{eN} = 1 - \frac{1}{2 \ln (b/a)}$$

(35a)

Notice that, if $b \gg a$, the electron current is much larger than the positive ion current. The situation would, of course, be reversed if the inner electrode were negative instead of positive.

3.7 Edge Effects. We have assumed thus far that the electrons and ions are sufficiently far from the boundary of the sensitive volume that no appreciable charge is induced on the guard electrode. When the charged particles are near the boundary of the sensitive volume, whether inside or outside of it, they will induce a charge both on the collecting electrode and on the guard electrode, and the pulse can no longer be computed in the simple manner outlined in Sec. 3.1.

The theory of "edge effects" has been developed for the simple case of a parallel-plate chamber, with the collecting electrode and the guard electrode as two infinite half planes joining along a straight line (see Fig. 3.5). This ideal case gives an adequate approximation of a parallel-plate chamber, in which the linear dimensions of the electrodes are large compared with their separation.

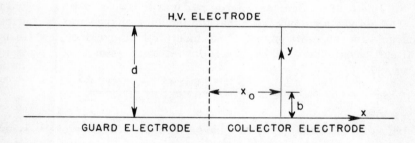

Fig. 3.5 — Diagram for calculation of the edge effects.

Consider a point charge in the space between the plates. Using as a frame of reference a cartesian system of coordinates, set the origin on the plane containing the collecting electrode and the guard electrode, the y axis perpendicular to this plane and passing through the point charge, the z axis parallel, and the x axis perpendicular to the boundary between the collecting electrode and the guard electrode. The problem consists in determining the surface density $\omega(x,z)$ of the charge induced in the x,z plane and integrating this function separately over the half-plane forming the collecting electrode and over the half-plane forming the guard electrode. The mathematical procedure is simplified by the observation that the ratio between charges induced on the two electrodes is obviously the same for all charges lying on a line parallel to their boundaries. Therefore we may substitute for the point charge a line charge of uniform density parallel to the z axis, calculate the surface density of the induced charge for this case, and then integrate along the x axis alone in order to determine the total charge induced on the two electrodes. The charge per unit length should, of course, be so chosen as to give the correct total charge on the x,z plane. As shown below, this is done by making it equal to the charge e of the particle.

The problem of determining the electric field of a line charge between two conducting planes parallel to it has been solved.* From the expression for the electric field is obtained the following expression for the surface density of the charge.

$$\omega(x) = -\frac{e}{2d} \frac{\sin(\pi b/d)}{\cosh(\pi x/d) - \cos(\pi b/d)} \tag{36}$$

In this equation d is the separation of the plates, b is the y coordinate of the line charge, and the charge per unit length is taken as equal to e. The minus sign indicates that the inducing charge and the induced charge have opposite signs. The indefinite integral of $\omega(x)$ is not difficult to calculate and has the following expression

$$\int \omega(x)\, dx = -\frac{e}{\pi} \tan^{-1}\left[\frac{e^{\pi x/d} - \cos(\pi b/d)}{\sin(\pi b/d)}\right] \tag{37}$$

Let x_0 be the distance of the charge from the boundary of the sensitive volume (positive if the charge is inside this volume). The total charge induced on the x,z plane is given by

$$Q = \int_{-\infty}^{+\infty} \omega(x)\, dx = -e\left(1 - \frac{b}{d}\right) \tag{38}$$

while the charge induced on the collecting electrode is given by

$$Q_c = \int_{-x_0}^{\infty} \omega(x)\, dx = -e\left\{\frac{1}{2} - \frac{1}{\pi} \tan^{-1}\left[\frac{e^{-\pi x_0/d} - \cos(\pi b/d)}{\sin(\pi b/d)}\right]\right\} \tag{39}$$

Notice that Q becomes equal to $-e$ when b = 0, which shows that the correct normalization factor has been chosen. The charge Q_c is a function of the ratios b/d and x_0/d. A graphical representation of this function is given in Fig. 3.6.

---

*See Smyth, "Static and Dynamic Electricity," McGraw-Hill Book Company, Inc., New York, 1939, pp. 83-84.

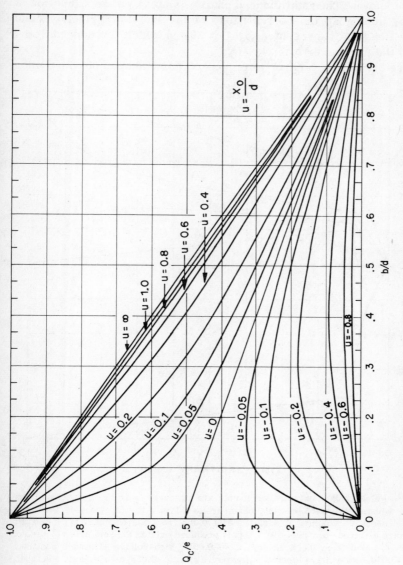

Fig. 3.6 — Fractional charge Q_c/e induced on collecting electrode of a parallel-plate chamber by a point charge e as a function of its distance x_0 from the boundary of the active volume and of its distance b from the collecting electrode; d is the depth of the chamber (see Fig. 3.5) and $u = x_0/d$.

The shape of the pulse produced by an ionizing particle traversing the chamber near the boundary of the sensitive volume can be calculated immediately if the drift velocities of the electrons and positive ions are known. The total induced charge is obtained, as a function of time, by adding up the contributions of the individual electrons and positive ions as represented by Eq. 39, in which Q_c depends on t through the parameter b.

Figure 3.7 shows various examples of pulse shapes obtained when

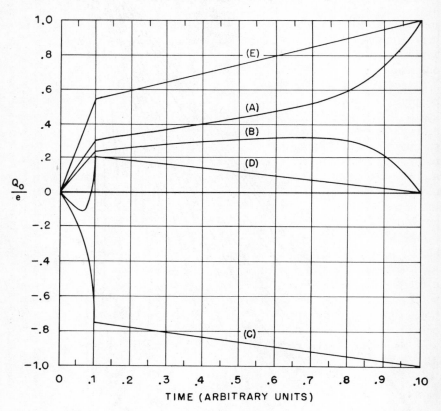

Fig. 3.7 — Pulse shapes obtained when ions are produced near the boundary of the sensitive volume of a parallel-plate chamber (see Fig. 3.5). (A) Ion pair produced inside the sensitive volume, at a distance of 0.05d from the boundary ($x_0 = +0.05d$); high-voltage electrode positive. (B) Ion pair produced outside the sensitive volume, at a distance of 0.05d from the boundary ($x_0 = -0.05d$); high-voltage electrode positive. (C) $x_0 = +0.05d$; high-voltage electrode negative. (D) $x_0 = -0.05d$, high-voltage electrode negative. (E) Ion pair produced at a large distance from the edge of the collecting electrode; high-voltage electrode positive (for comparison). In all cases the ion pair is supposed to be produced half way between the plates (b = d/2). The drift velocity of the electrons is taken as equal to 10 times that of the positive ions in order to make a graphical representation of the pulse shape possible.

an ion pair is formed inside or outside the sensitive volume at a small distance from its boundary. In order to make a graphical representation possible, the drift velocity of the positive ions has been taken as one-tenth as large, instead of about one-thousandth as large, as the free electrons. For comparison, the pulse produced by an ion pair formed inside the sensitive volume at a great distance from the boundary is also represented in Fig. 3.7. Note that the total charge induced on the collecting electrode after both the electron and the positive ion have been collected is always e when the ion pair has been formed inside the sensitive volume and is always zero when the ion pair has been formed outside it. The pulse shape, however, varies greatly with the position of the original ion pair and with the polarity of the chamber.

Effect of Diffusion on Pulse Height. The effect of diffusion on the response of an ionization chamber to a variable source of ionization has thus far been disregarded. The role of diffusion is always negligible as far as the motion of heavy ions is concerned, but it may have an appreciable influence on the signal produced by the motion of electrons. Electrons may diffuse in or out of the sensitive volume when a density gradient exists at the boundary of this volume. Moreover, electrons formed near the negative electrode may diffuse back to it instead of reaching the positive electrode. Let us calculate the probability of back-diffusion for the case of an ion pair formed at the distance x_1 from the negative electrode of a parallel-plate ion chamber. From physical reasons, it is obvious that this probability is identical with the fractional number of electrons entering the negative electrode when uniform ionization is produced at a constant rate within an infinitely thin layer parallel to the electrodes and at a distance x_1 from the negative electrode. The problem is thus reduced to one of the type discussed in Chap. 2, Sec. 2.3. The current vector j^- and the density n^- satisfy the following equations (see Chap. 2, Eqs. 21 and 22).

$$j^- = n^- w^- + D^- \frac{dn^-}{dx}$$

$$-\frac{dj^-}{dx} = \frac{N}{S} \delta (x - d + x_1)$$

where d is the depth of the chamber, x the distance from the positive electrode, N is the number of ion pairs produced within the sensitive volume per unit time, S is the area of the collecting electrode, and δ indicates the δ function. These equations, together with the condition of continuity for n^- at $x = d - x_1$ and with the boundary conditions

$$n^- = 0 \quad \text{for } x = 0 \text{ and } x = d$$

yield the following expressions for n^-:

$$n^- = \frac{N}{S} \frac{1}{w^-} \frac{1 - e^{-(w^-/D^-)x_1}}{1 - e^{-(w^-/D^-)d}} \left[1 - e^{-(w^-/D^-)x} \right]$$

for $0 < x < d - x_1$

$$n^- = \frac{N}{S} \frac{1}{w^-} \frac{e^{-(w^-/D^-)x_1} - e^{-(w^-/D^-)d}}{1 - e^{-(w^-/D^-)d}} \left[e^{(w^-/D^-)(d-x)} - 1 \right] \tag{40}$$

for $d - x_1 < x < d$

The number of electrons entering the negative electrode per square centimeter per second can be expressed by

$$\left| j^-(d) \right| = \frac{N}{S} \frac{e^{-(w^-/D^-)x_1} - e^{-(w^-/D^-)d}}{1 - e^{-(w^-/D^-)d}}$$

Since the number of electrons produced per square centimeter per second is N/S, the probability of back-diffusion, $p(x_1)$, is given by the equation

$$p(x_1) = \frac{e^{-(w^-/D^-)x_1} - e^{-(w^-/D^-)d}}{1 - e^{-(w^-/D^-)d}} \tag{41}$$

From Eq. 18, Chap. 1, noting that in all practical cases $(w^-/D^-)d = Ed/0.025\,\epsilon^-$ is a large number, the expression for p becomes

$$p(x_1) = e^{-V_1/0.025\,\epsilon^-} \tag{42}$$

where $V_1 = Ex_1$ is the difference of potential between the place of production of the electrons and the negative electrode.

Consider now N_0 ion pairs produced at the distance x_1 from the negative electrode. If diffusion is neglected, the computed value for the height of the pulse caused by the motion of the electrons is (see Secs. 3.3 and 3.5)

$$P_0 = N_0 W_0 \left(1 - \frac{x_1}{d} \right)$$

If back-scattering is considered, the pulse height becomes

$$P = N_0 W_0 \left[1 - p(x_1)\right]\left(1 - \frac{x_1}{d}\right) - N_0 W_0 p(x_1)\, \frac{x_1}{d}$$

since the electrons that go to the negative electrode produce a pulse proportional to x_1/d and of sign opposite to that of the electrons going to the positive electrodes. Usually $p(x_1)$ has an appreciable value only for very small values of x_1, so that the product $p(x_1)(x_1/d)$ is negligible. Therefore the fractional decrease in pulse height caused by diffusion is expressed by

$$\frac{P_0 - P}{P_0} = p(x_1) = e^{-V_1/0.025} \tag{43}$$

3.8 **Testing of "Fast" Ionization Chambers.** For many purposes, some of which will be mentioned below, it is often desirable to determine experimentally the function $f(t)$ for a given chamber and for a given distribution of the ionization. As previously explained, this can be done either by (1) studying the shape of voltage pulses produced by single ionizing particles, or by (2) investigating the time dependence of the electron current upon a sudden turning on or off of a source of continuous ionization.

Experiments of the first type can be carried out with the arrangement schematically represented in Fig. 3.8. CH is the ionization

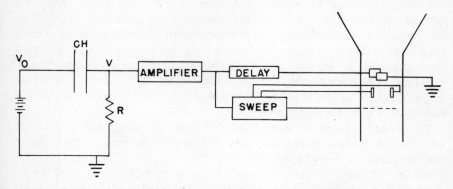

Fig. 3.8—Experimental arrangement for testing "fast" ionization chambers with α particles.

chamber, which contains a suitable source of α particles. The pulse V at the collecting electrode is amplified electronically and then applied to one of the vertical deflecting plates of a cathode-ray oscilloscope through a delay line, which delays the pulse by several microseconds without changing its shape appreciably. The pulse at the output of the amplifier is used to trigger the sweep circuit. This circuit provides a positive square pulse, which is applied to the intensifier electrode of the cathode ray tube, normally biased below cutoff, and turns the beam on for the duration of the pulse. The sweep circuit also provides a saw-tooth pulse, which is applied in push-pull to the horizontal deflecting plates thus producing a linear sweep of appropriate speed. For each α particle entering the chamber, a trace representing the output voltage V_e as a function of time appears on the oscilloscope screen. The delay line between the amplifier and the vertical deflecting plate makes it possible to study the beginning of the pulse, which otherwise could not be observed because of the small unavoidable delay in starting the sweep circuit. $V_e(t)$ is related by Eq. 23 to the function $X(t)$, which defines the transient response of the detecting equipment. If the rise time of the amplifier is sufficiently small and its resolving time is sufficiently long, so that the transient response of the amplifier may be approximated with a step function [$\psi(t) = 0$ for $t < 0$; $\psi(t) = $ const. for $t > 0$], this equation together with Eq. 24 yields

$$V_e(t) = \text{const.} \int_0^t f(t_1)\, dt_1$$

The arrangement described was used for determining the shape of the pulses produced by polonium α particles in the parallel-plate chamber represented in Fig. 3.9. The α particles were projected across the sensitive volume of the chamber in a direction parallel to the plates. Hence, disregarding edge effects, for an ideal transient response of the amplifier the output voltage will rise linearly with time until all electrons are collected and then remain practically constant. The time for collection of the electrons is, of course, equal to the distance of the track from the positive electrode divided by the drift velocity of the electrons.

The results obtained were used for the determination of the drift velocity in various gases and gas mixtures. The values thus found are included in the graphs given in Chap. 1, Figs. 1.3 to 1.6. The accuracy claimed for these values is not very high because of some distortion of the pulse shape produced by the electronic circuit and by the edge effects.

Through a study of α-particle pulses it is possible, at least in principle, to determine whether or not any electron attachment takes place. This can be done by measuring the ratio between the "fast" part of the pulse (due to the motion of free electrons) and the "slow"

part of the pulse (due to the motion of ions). In a parallel-plate chamber with the beam of α particles parallel to the plates this ratio should
be equal to the ratio between the distances of the beam from the positive and the negative electrodes, respectively, if there is no electron
attachment. Any electron attachment leading to the formation of slow-
moving negative ions will decrease the fast and increase the slow part
of the pulse. No measurements of electron attachment were carried
out by the method outlined above, mainly because no amplifier was
available which could amplify without distortion both the slow and the
fast part of the pulse.

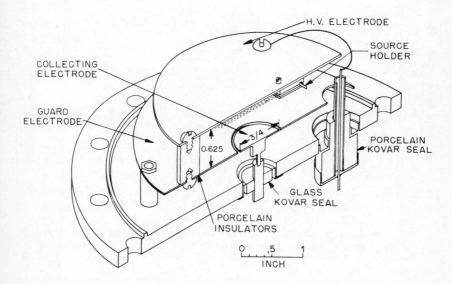

Fig. 3.9 — Inner construction of chamber used for determining the shape of α-particle
pulses.

With the arrangement described, the dependence of the size of the
electron pulse on the voltage difference across the chamber was
measured for several gases. A change of pulse height with voltage
is proof that either electron attachment or recombination takes place
(except at very low voltages, at which diffusion may play some role;
see Sec. 3.7, Effect of Diffusion on Pulse Height). It is possible to
distinguish between the two phenomena by comparing measurements
with ionizing particles of different specific ionization. The probability
of attachment is independent of the density of ionization, while the
probability of recombination is proportional to it.

As an example, the two curves in Fig. 3.10 give electron-pulse heights versus electric-field strength as obtained with the chamber filled with argon and with boron trifluoride. The fact that the curve

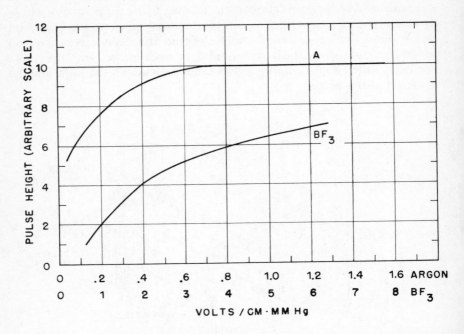

Fig. 3.10 — Pulse height as a function of E/p in argon (840 mm Hg pressure) and BF_3 (388 mm Hg pressure). Measurements taken with the chamber represented in Fig. 3.9.

for argon becomes horizontal for E/p > 0.7 is taken as an indication that in argon attachment and recombination already become negligible at very moderate fields. The fact that the curve for boron trifluoride continues to rise, at least up to E/p = 6, is interpreted by the assumption that in boron trifluoride a large amount of attachment takes place even at comparatively large fields. The behavior of the curve for boron trifluoride depends critically on the origin of the gas, indicating that the capture is due, at least partly, to impurities rather than to the boron trifluoride itself.

The experimental arrangement for the second type of measurement mentioned at the beginning of the present section is schematically represented in Fig. 3.11. X represents an x-ray tube in which the beam intensity can be controlled by means of a grid placed in front of the cathode. CH is the ionization chamber to be investigated. Since the x-ray tube is operated at comparatively low voltage (about 40 kv), a window covered with thin metal foil must be provided in the wall of the chamber in order to admit the soft x-ray beam. The voltage drop across the leak resistor R, after suitable amplification, is applied to the vertical deflecting plates of a cathode-ray oscilloscope. The sweep circuit provides a square positive pulse, used to turn on the beam of the oscilloscope, and a saw-tooth pulse, to give a horizontal linear sweep. The sweep circuit also provides a square negative pulse, the beginning of which can be delayed by an adjustable amount

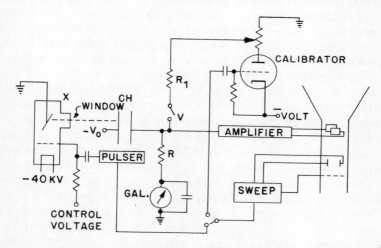

Fig. 3.11—Experimental arrangement for testing "fast" chambers with a modulated x-ray source.

with respect to the beginning of the sweep. The sweep circuit can either be made to operate automatically at a rate of the order of 100 sweeps per second or it may be triggered manually so as to give single sweeps. The delayed signal from the sweep circuit may be used to trigger the circuit marked "Pulser," the purpose of which is to turn on or off the x-ray beam by suddenly raising or lowering the voltage of the control grid. When the pulser is connected and the sweep circuit operated, there will appear on the oscilloscope screen a trace which gives the output voltage V_e as a function of time subsequent to the sudden turning on or off of the ionizing beam. $V_e(t)$ is given by Eq. 26, which, in the case of a constant source of ionization turned on at the time t = 0, yields

$$V_e(t) = eN \int_0^t X(t_1) \, dt_1$$

If the resolving time of the amplifier is sufficiently small, the function $\psi(t)$ can be approximated by a δ function and, according to Eq. 24, $X(t) = f(t)$. The above equation then becomes

$$V_e(t) = \text{const.} \int_0^t f(t_1) \, dt_1$$

This method for testing chambers is superior in many ways to that described previously which makes use of α-particle pulses. Successive pulses obtained by turning on or cutting off the x-ray beam are identical, while α-particle pulses always differ somewhat from one another because a beam of α particles is never perfectly collimated and may not be perfectly monoenergetic. It is possible, furthermore, to calibrate the x-ray equipment so as to determine very accurately the fraction of the ionization current carried by the electrons. The following procedure is used. With the x-ray tube running at a constant intensity, the ionization current $I_0 = I_0^+ + I_0^-$ is measured by means of a galvanometer in series with the leak resistor R. Then the sweep circuit is operated manually, cutting off the x-ray beam, and the size of the fast pulse appearing on the oscilloscope screen is recorded. The height of this pulse is proportional to the intensity of the electron current I_0^-. Then the x-ray tube is turned off, and a current equal to the ionization current previously measured is sent through the leak resistor R by connecting its upper end through another resistor R_1 ($R_1 \gg R$) to an appropriate point along the plate resistor of the tube marked "Calibrator." The output of the sweep circuit giving a delayed square negative pulse is disconnected from the x-ray pulser and connected to the grid of the calibrator tube. When the sweep circuit is operated, the delayed negative pulse turns off the calibrator tube and interrupts the current through the leak resistor. The height of the pulse appearing on the oscilloscope screen is proportional to the intensity of the current originally present in R, which is equal to the total ionization current $I_0^+ + I_0^-$. Hence, the ratio between the sizes of the pulses obtained by turning off the x-ray beam and by cutting off the calibrator current will be equal to the ratio $I_0^-/(I_0^+ + I_0^-)$ of the electron current to the total ionization current. Experience has shown that the fractional value of the electron current can be determined to within 1 or 2 per cent by this method.

The testing equipment described above was used to investigate the response of a parallel-plate chamber uniformly irradiated over its sensitive volume. The construction of this chamber is represented in Fig. 3.12.

A photographic record of the oscilloscope deflection obtained by turning on the x-ray beam is reproduced in Fig. 3.13. The chamber

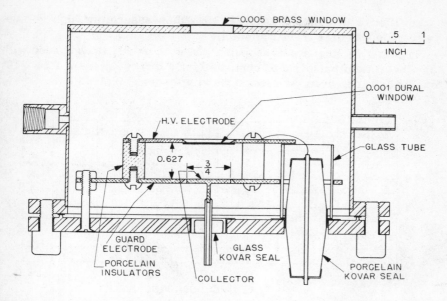

Fig. 3.12—Chamber used for the tests with the pulsed x-ray source. X rays are admitted into the sensitive volume through the 0.005-in. brass window in the outer case and the 0.001-in. dural window in the high-voltage electrode.

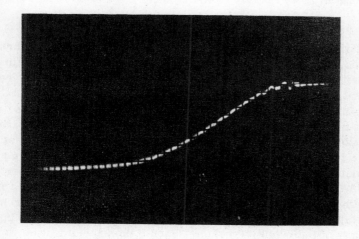

Fig. 3.13—Oscilloscope record obtained with the arrangement shown in Fig. 3.10. The total duration of the sweep is approximately 1.5 μsec. Repetition rate is about 100 per sec; exposure about 2 sec. The small oscillation at the beginning of the pulse is caused by electric pickup from the circuit which turns on the x-ray beam.

was filled with purified argon at 1.8 atm pressure; the high-voltage electrode was kept at −1,000 volts.

In Fig. 3.14, the observed pulse shape, curve 3, is compared with the theoretical pulse shape computed for a drift velocity of 1.35×10^6 cm/sec, which gives the closest fit with the experimental data.

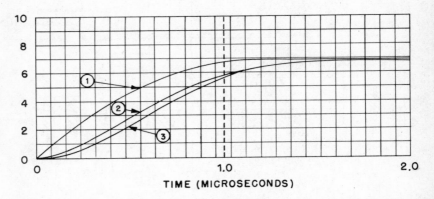

Fig. 3.14 — Comparison between computed and observed pulse shapes for the parallel-plate chamber represented in Fig. 3.12. A constant source of ionization is turned on at the time t = 0. (1) Electron current in the chamber, computed for a drift velocity of 1.35×10^6 cm/sec (separation of the plates, 1.57 cm). (2) Voltage at the output of the amplifier, computed for a value RC = 0.24 μsec of the input time constant, taking into account the frequency response of the amplifier. (3) Observed output voltage (from Fig. 3.13).

According to Eq. 32, when the x-ray beam is suddenly turned on, the electron current increases as a quadratic function of the time until the electrons formed at t = 0 have been collected and then remains constant. This behavior is represented by curve 1, Fig. 3.14. Curve 2 represents the output pulse corresponding to the current pulse represented by curve 1 and computed by taking into account the transient response of the amplifier, the resolving time of which was approximately 2.4×10^{-7} sec. One sees that the agreement between experimental and theoretical pulse shapes is satisfactory if not perfect. A possible explanation for the difference between curves 2 and 3 may be found in the edge effects (see Sec. 3.7) since, as it is apparent from the design of the chamber (Fig. 3.12), the gas was irradiated up to the boundary of the sensitive volume. Should the experiment be repeated, this source of error could be minimized by providing uniform irradiation of the gas not only within the sensitive volume, but also outside of this volume, to a distance from its boundary comparable with the separation of the plates.

The experiment described may be considered as a check of the theoretical predictions of the operation of the chamber or, alternately, as a method for the determination of the drift velocity of electrons. The values of the drift velocity obtained with this method are included in the graphs given in Chap. 1, Fig. 1.3.

The pulsed x-ray equipment was also used for the determination of the fraction of electron current in cylindrical ionization chambers filled with mixtures of argon and CO_2 (see Chap. 5, Sec. 5.4). The experimental results were in very close agreement with the theoretical predictions, indicating that the electron attachment was negligible.

3.9 <u>Statistical Fluctuations of the Ionization Current</u>. When a chamber is connected to a fast amplifier and irradiated with a strong source, the output voltage exhibits fluctuations which are considerably larger than those due to the tube noise. These fluctuations are caused by statistical fluctuations in the intensity of the ionization current. An approximate estimate of their magnitude can be obtained as follows: Let τ be the resolving time of the detecting equipment, determined by the time for collection of electrons in the chamber, by the input time constant RC, and by the frequency response of the amplifier. We may assume that the instantaneous value of the output voltage is proportional to the number of ion pairs produced in the chamber in a time equal to τ, and that this number, in turn, is proportional to the number of ionizing particles traversing the chamber during time τ. If I is the intensity of the ionization current and m is the average number of ion pairs produced by each particle in the chamber, the average number of particles traversing the chamber during the time τ is given by $I\tau/me$. This number undergoes statistical fluctuations, the root mean square of which has the relative value $1/\sqrt{I\tau/me}$. This quantity represents also the relative value of the root-mean-square fluctuation of the output voltage, indicated by $\Delta V/V$. Hence

$$\frac{\Delta V}{V} = \sqrt{\frac{me}{I\tau}} \tag{44}$$

Some experiments were carried out to check the above relation. In these experiments, eight cylindrical chambers of the type which will be described in Chap. 5, Sec. 5.4 were used. These chambers were 18 in. in length and 2 in. in diameter and were filled with a mixture of argon and carbon dioxide to a pressure of 4.5 atm. They were all connected in parallel and their total capacity, including that of the connecting cables and the amplifier input, was approximately 100 $\mu\mu$f. The leak resistor had a value of 1,000 ohms; thus the input time constant was 10^{-7} sec. The chambers were irradiated with a strong γ-ray source. A galvanometer, in series with the leak resistor and by-passed by a large condenser, was used to measure the ionization current. The voltage drop across the resistor was applied to the input of a fast amplifier (70 per cent gain at 4 megacycles). The variable component of the output voltage was measured by means of a bolometric arrangement, which gave directly the mean-square value of the fluctuations.

The experimental results are summarized in Figs. 3.15 and 3.16. Figure 3.15 represents the mean-square value of the fluctuations as a

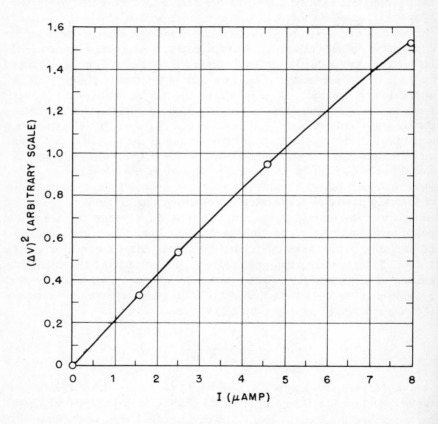

Fig. 3.15 — Average square fluctuation of the output voltage $(\Delta V)^2$ as a function of the intensity I of ionization current; eight cylindrical chambers in parallel (see description in Sec. 5.4) operated at 2,000 volts.

function of the current in the chambers. The voltage across the chambers was 2,000 volts; the ionization current was changed by varying the distance between the source and the bank of chambers. According to Eq. 44, $(\Delta V)^2$ is given by

$$(\Delta V)^2 = \frac{V^2 me}{I\tau} = R^2 I \frac{me}{\tau} \qquad (44a)$$

which indicates that $(\Delta V)^2$ should be proportional to I, if τ is constant.

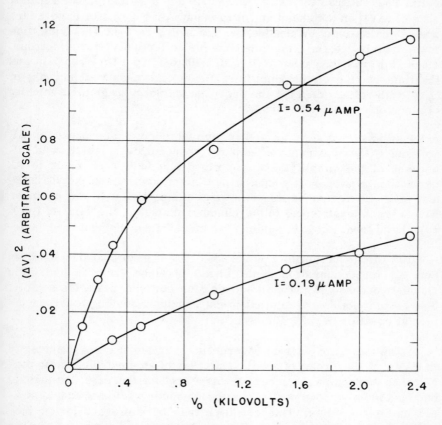

Fig. 3.16 — Average square fluctuation of the output voltage $(\Delta V)^2$ as a function of the voltage V_0 across the chambers for two different intensities of radiation. In both cases the ionization currents reach their saturation values (I = 0.54 and I = 0.19 μamp, respectively) in the neighborhood of 400 volts.

The curve in Fig. 3.15 shows that this is approximately the case, at least as long as the ionization current is not too large. For large values of the ionization current, a deviation from the proportionality law becomes apparent. It is possible that this deviation may be caused by space-charge effects which decrease the field in the chambers, thereby increasing the time for collection of electrons.

Figure 3.16 gives $(\Delta V)^2$ as a function of the voltage applied to the chambers for two fixed positions of the γ-ray source. In both cases, the ionization currents reached their saturation values at about 400 volts. These saturation values were 0.19 and 0.54 μamp. The dependence of $(\Delta V)^2$ on the chamber voltage shown in Fig. 3.16 can be interpreted qualitatively by considering that in this case the resolving time τ was mainly determined by the time for collection of the electrons, since this was long compared with both the input time constant and the time of rise of the amplifier. Hence, the observed increase of $(\Delta V)^2$ with voltage reflects the increase of the average drift velocity of electrons in the chambers.

Equation 44 may be expected to give the correct dependence of ΔV on I and τ, but it cannot be used for an accurate calculation of ΔV because of the simplifying assumptions that have been made in its derivation. However, if τ equals the time of rise of the output pulse and m is calculated by assuming that all particles in the chamber have a track length equal to the chamber diameter, the value of $(\Delta V)^2$ calculated from Eq. 44 is within a factor of 2 from the observed value.

3.10 Limits of Validity of the Theory. The method developed in Sec. 3.1 for computation of the signal obtained from an ionization chamber breaks down when the ionization current varies too rapidly. Two assumptions were implicit in the argument leading to the fundamental equation (Eq. 8), namely:

(1) The ionization current undergoes negligible changes of intensity in times of the order of the transit time of an electromagnetic disturbance through the chamber. If this were not the case, the signals obtained from various portions of the chamber would not add up simply, as Eq. 8 implies. This condition may be expressed by the inequality

$$\frac{l}{c} \frac{dI}{dt} \ll I \qquad (45)$$

where l represents the largest linear dimension of the chamber and c is the velocity of light.

(2) The variations of the magnetic energy must be sufficiently small so that they may be neglected in the energy balance. If W_m represents the magnetic energy, this condition is expressed by the inequality

$$\frac{dW_m}{dt} \ll V_0 I \qquad (46)$$

Now W_m is of the order of $h l^2 H^2$ where h represents the separation of the electrodes, l their linear dimension, and H is some average value of the magnetic field. In turn, H is of the order of $l ej/c = I/lc$. (For example, $\pi l ej/c$ is the field at the edge of a circular parallel-plate chamber of diameter l, in which the ionization current has a constant density ej.) Hence the condition expressed in Eq. 46 may be rewritten as

$$\frac{h}{c^2} \frac{dI^2}{dt} \ll V_0 I$$

or

$$\frac{l^2}{c^2} \frac{dI}{dt} \ll \frac{V_0 l^2}{h} \qquad (46a)$$

Clearly, if Eq. 45 is satisfied, Eq. 46a is satisfied as well, at least in all practical cases. In fact the condition expressed by Eq. 45 gives (l^2/c^2) $(dI/dt) \ll (l/c)$ I. The quantity $(l/c)I$ represents the charge carried by the ionization current during the transit time of an electromagnetic disturbance through the chamber. This is always small compared with the quantity $(l^2/h)V_0$, which represents, apart from a numerical factor, the charge present on the electrodes due to the field existing between them. Therefore condition (1) is not only necessary but also, in all practical cases, sufficient for the validity of the theory developed.

As indicated in Chap. 1, the drift velocities not only of ions but also of free electrons are always very small compared with the velocity of light. This means that in the case of an instantaneous burst of ionization, the ionization current will set in suddenly and subsequently vary with time at a rate sufficiently slow to ensure the validity of our approximation. Even though the theory developed does not make it possible to calculate the current I for a time of the order of l/c after the production of the ionization burst, the fact remains that it will give correct results for all subsequent times.

3.11 Very Rapidly Rising Ionization Pulse. The theory is inadequate for the solution of a practical problem only in the case of a signal produced by a source of ionization whose intensity increases very rapidly with time. In this case one must start from Maxwell's equations

$$\text{curl } \vec{E} = -\frac{1}{c}\frac{\partial \vec{H}}{\partial t}$$

$$\text{curl } \vec{H} = \frac{1}{c}\frac{\partial \vec{E}}{\partial t} + 4\pi e(n^+\vec{w}^+ - n^-\vec{w}^-)$$

$$\text{div } \vec{E} = 4\pi e(n^+ - n^-)$$

$$\text{div } \vec{H} = 0$$

(47)

The following simplifying assumptions are made:

1. The electromagnetic signal produced by the ionization is small compared with the preexisting static electric field. This means that $\vec{w}^+$ and $\vec{w}^-$ may be considered as given functions of the position.

2. Recombination and attachment are negligible. This condition becomes less restrictive as the pulse becomes faster. It means that the ion and electron densities n^+ and n^-, and the corresponding drift velocities, $\vec{w}^+$ and $\vec{w}^-$ are related by the equations

$$\frac{\partial n^+}{\partial t} = n_0 - \text{div}\left[n^+\vec{w}^+ - D^+ \text{ grad } n^+\right]$$

$$\frac{\partial n^-}{\partial t} = n_0 - \text{div}\left[n^-\vec{w}^- - D^- \text{ grad } n^-\right]$$

(48)

where n_0 represents the number of ion pairs produced per second and per unit volume at a given position. As a consequence of the first assumption, Eqs. 48 are not connected with Eqs. 47 and may be solved separately, with the boundary conditions that $n^+ = 0$ at the positive electrode and $n^- = 0$ at the negative electrode. The values thus found from Eqs. 48 can then be introduced in Eqs. 47.

As an example, consider the case where the intensity of the ionizing radiation increases exponentially with time so that

$$n_0(x,y,z,t) = \psi(x,y,z)\, e^{t/\tau}$$

Since Eqs. 48 are linear in n^+ and n^-, and since the only term that depends on the time explicitly is an exponential function of the time, solutions exist in which n^+ and n^- depend on the time as $e^{t/\tau}$. These solutions satisfy the correct initial conditions if we assume that n^+ and n^- are zero before the beginning of the ionization pulse ($t = -\infty$). This means that the only terms that depend explicitly on time in Maxwell's equations (Eqs. 47) are, again, exponential functions of the type $e^{t/\tau}$. As a consequence, the vectors $\vec{E}$ and $\vec{H}$, which describe the electromagnetic disturbance produced by the pulse, also vary with time as $e^{t/\tau}$, provided only that they are assumed to be zero before the ionization pulse begins. The conclusion is that, under the slightly restrictive conditions set forth above, a source of ionization whose intensity increases exponentially with time will always produce in an ionization chamber a signal that exhibits the same time dependence as the intensity itself.*

In many practical cases, diffusion may be neglected. If the signal is very short, the terms div $(n^+\vec{w}^+)$ and div $(n^-\vec{w}^-)$ in Eq. 48 may also be neglected; then n^+ and n^-, assuming that they are both zero at the time $t = 0$, are given by the equations

$$n^+(x,y,z,t) = n^-(x,y,z,t) = \int_0^t n_0(x,y,z,t_1)\, dt_1 \qquad (49)$$

This means that in Maxwell's equations the density of charge may be regarded as zero and the density of current as a given function of time and position.

As a practical application, consider the following problem: A coaxial line of infinite length consisting of two conducting cylinders is filled with a gas, so that it forms an ionization chamber. The two cylinders are at different voltages. Assume that the outer cylinder is positive.

For the description of the field, a cylindrical system of coordinates (r,θ,z) will be used, with the z axis along the axis of the line.

Assume that a section of the line of very small length Δ and situated at $z = 0$ is uniformly ionized by an external agent. Assume, furthermore, that the drift velocities of ions and electrons are proportional to the electric field, and therefore inversely proportional to the r coordinate. This means that the current density in the ionized layer is inversely proportional to r, so its absolute value is given by an expression of the form

$$ej = e\,|\vec{j}^+ - \vec{j}^-| = \frac{a}{r}\,ej_a \qquad (50)$$

---

*It can easily be shown that, while the absence of recombination is an essential condition for the validity of this result, the absence of attachment is not.

where a is the radius of the inner tube and j_a is the value of j_a at the surface of this electrode. If $w_a{}^+$ and $w_a{}^-$ are the absolute values of the drift velocities at the same place, j_a is given by

$$j_a(t) = (w_a{}^+ + w_a{}^-) \int_0^t n_0(t_1) \, dt_1 \qquad (51)$$

It is well-known that in a coaxial line made of two perfectly conducting cylinders separated by an uncharged dielectric of dielectric constant equal to 1, Maxwell's equations have solutions in which the electric vector has only an r component E_r, while the magnetic vector has only a θ component, H_θ. E_r and H_θ are equal in magnitude and are given by equations of the type

$$E_r = H_\theta = \frac{1}{r} f_1\left(t - \frac{z}{c}\right) \qquad (52)$$

or

$$E_r = -H_\theta = \frac{1}{r} f_2\left(t + \frac{z}{c}\right) \qquad (53)$$

Equation 52 represents a transverse wave propagating with light velocity c in the direction of the positive z axis. Equation 53 represents a transverse wave propagating with the same velocity in the negative direction.

Under the assumptions made above, the ionization pulse will produce two waves of this type propagating in opposite directions from the ionized layer. To demonstrate this, we need only prove that the boundary conditions at z = 0 can be satisfied by assuming the electromagnetic field to be represented by equations of the type of Eq. 52 for z > 0, and by equations of the type of Eq. 53 for z < 0. These boundary conditions state that $\vec{E}$ is continuous across the ionized layer, while the value of $\vec{H}$ changes by $4\pi/c$ times the surface density of current in the ionized layer. Since we have assumed that the outer conductor is positive, this current points toward the inner conductor, and the boundary conditions give the equations

$$\frac{1}{r} f_1(t) - \frac{1}{r} f_2(t) = 0$$

$$\frac{1}{r} f_1(t) + \frac{1}{r} f_2(t) = \frac{4\pi}{c} \Delta \frac{a}{r} e j_a$$

These equations may be satisfied for all values of z if

$$f_1(t) = f_2(t) = \frac{2\pi}{c}\, \Delta\, aej_a(t)$$

The solution of the problem is therefore

$$E_r = H_\theta = \frac{2\pi}{c}\, \Delta\, \frac{a}{r}\, ej_a\left(t - \frac{z}{c}\right) \qquad \text{for } z > 0$$

$$E_r = -H_\theta = \frac{2\pi}{c}\, \Delta\, \frac{a}{r}\, ej_a\left(t + \frac{z}{c}\right) \qquad \text{for } z < 0$$

$$(54)$$

The current I in the inner tube can be calculated from the equation

$$4\pi I = 2\pi r H_\theta \qquad (55)$$

Together with Eqs. 54 this gives

$$I(z,t) = \frac{\pi}{c}\, \Delta\, aej_a\left(t - \frac{z}{c}\right) \qquad \text{for } z > 0$$

$$I(z,t) = -\frac{\pi}{c}\, \Delta\, aej_a\left(t + \frac{z}{c}\right) \qquad \text{for } z < 0$$

$$(56)$$

The quantity $2\pi a\Delta j_a$ represents the total charge flowing from the ionized layer into the inner conductor per unit time. Hence, Eqs. 56 mean simply that the current entering the pipe at $z = 0$ splits into two equal parts that propagate with light velocity in opposite directions.

If the ionized layer is not infinitely thin, as is assumed above, then the solution of the problem can be obtained by subdividing the ionized layer into an infinite number of infinitely thin layers and taking the sum (i.e., the integral) of the solutions corresponding to the elementary layers.

Chapter 4

GAS MULTIPLICATION

4.1 General Considerations. When in a portion of the volume of an ionization chamber, the electric-field strength exceeds a certain value, the electrons that penetrate this volume will acquire, between collisions, a sufficient energy to ionize the gas molecules. Thus more electrons will be liberated, which in turn will produce more ionization by collision. Finally all electrons, whether produced directly by the external ionizing agent or generated by secondary collision processes, will reach the positive electrode.

This phenomenon is called "gas multiplication." It is often used to amplify the effects of weakly ionizing radiations. The chambers to be operated with gas multiplication are usually in the shape of a hollow cylinder, with a thin wire stretched along the axis. The wire is always positive with respect to the cylinder and, when the difference of potential between the two electrodes is sufficiently large, there exists around the wire a cylindrical region where gas multiplication takes place. The diameter of this cylindrical region is usually a small multiple of the diameter of the wire. Thus its volume is very small compared with the volume of the chamber, so the probability of an electron being produced in it by the primary ionizing radiation is negligible. The electrons produced outside the region where gas multiplication takes place produce, on the average, an equal number of ion pairs by collision before reaching the wire. Let us denote this number by $n-1$, so that n represents the total number of electrons per primary ion pair in what we may call the "initial avalanche." In addition to the electrons set free by collisions, electrons may be produced by photoelectric effect, because ionization and excitation of the gas molecules by electron collision result in the emission of photons. Since the excitation energy is always smaller than the ionization energy, photoelectric effect can occur only on the cathode when the counter is filled with a pure gas. When, however, the counter is filled with a gas mixture, photons emitted by molecules of one gas may be able to ionize molecules of another. Let γ be the average number of photoelectrons produced per ion pair generated in the gas (where always $\gamma \ll 1$). Then the initial avalanche of n electrons will be accompanied by the production of γn photoelectrons, which will produce a secondary avalanche of γn^2 electrons. The argument may be repeated, and finally it gives the following expression for the total number M of electrons set free in the chamber when one ion pair is produced by an external agent

$$M = n + \gamma n^2 + \gamma^2 n^3 \ldots \qquad (1)$$

The value of γn depends on the voltage applied. When the voltage is sufficiently low so that $\gamma n < 1$, the chamber is said to be operated as a "proportional counter." The number M is called the "gas multiplication" and its value is given by

$$M = \frac{n}{1 - \gamma n} \qquad (1a)$$

This equation shows that, if n is sufficiently small, M is practically equal to n, which means that the photoelectric effect can be neglected.

If the voltage is such that $\gamma n \geq 1$, Eq. 1 gives $M = \infty$, which means physically that an electric breakdown occurs in the chamber. A chamber operated under these conditions is called a "discharge counter." The discharge may be inherently unstable, or it may be quenched by external means. Not much work was done at the Los Alamos Project on the development of discharge counters. This discussion will, therefore, be limited to the counters operating in the proportional region.

First, a proportional counter as defined above is not necessarily "proportional." In fact, the gas multiplication is a constant, i.e., independent of the primary ionization, only so long as one can neglect the modification of the electric field near the wire caused by the space charge. This is the case when both the primary ionization and the gas multiplication are sufficiently small. Assuming that this condition is fulfilled and, moreover, that no electron attachment takes place, the gas multiplication M, for a given gas, will be a function of the diameter a of the wire, of the diameter b of the cathode, of the pressure p, and of the voltage V_0 across the counter. If the photoelectric effect plays a role, M will also depend on the nature of the cathode. If, however, the photoelectric effect is negligible, which is always the case for sufficiently low values of the gas multiplication,

then the nature of the cathode is immaterial, and all significant phenomena take place at a small distance from the wire. Hence, if V_0
and b are changed without altering the field at the wire, M will not
change. Moreover, M will remain unchanged if a and b are multiplied
by a common factor k, if p is divided by the same factor, and if V_0
is kept constant. In this operation all linear dimensions, including
the mean free paths, are multiplied by the same factor k, while the
electric-field strength is divided by k. Thus the energy gained by the
electrons between collisions at corresponding points of the two counters is the same, and the number of collisions for electrons traveling
between two corresponding points of the two counters is also the
same. It follows that M can be expressed as a function of the ratio
$V_0/\ln (b/a)$ and of the product pa:

$$M = M \left[\frac{V_0}{\ln (b/a)} , \ pa \right] \qquad (2)$$

Let us now discuss qualitatively the time dependence of the pulse
given by a proportional counter. For simplicity, assume that the wire
is grounded through a resistance R, sufficiently large so that the
product RC of this resistance and C, the combined capacity of the
collecting electrode plus the input of the amplifier, represents a time
much longer than the duration of the pulse. Suppose now that N_0 ion
pairs are produced simultaneously at a given point in the counter.
The electrons will drift toward the wire, causing its potential to vary
by a small amount. As soon as the electrons reach the neighborhood
of the wire, gas multiplication takes place. In a very short time all
the electrons formed by collision will reach the wire, and during this
time the potential of the wire will undergo an appreciable change. At
the same time, the positive ions will start drifting away from the
wire, at first rapidly, then more and more slowly as they pass into
the region where the field is weaker. Thus the potential of the wire
will continue to change after all electrons have been captured, first
fairly rapidly, then very slowly. The pulse of the proportional counter may therefore be expected to exhibit a shape of the type shown in
Fig. 4.1. The "delay" t_1 in the beginning of the pulse depends, of
course, on the distance from the wire at which the original ions are
formed. If this distance is of the order of 1 cm, t_1 may be a few
tenths of a microsecond. The time interval $t_2 - t_1$ in which the gas
multiplication takes place and the electrons are swept away is only
a small fraction of a microsecond. The total time for the positive
ions to reach the cathode is of the order of a millisecond, but most of
the pulse due to the motion of the positive ions takes place in a much

shorter time, while the positive ions travel in the intense field near the wire. The contribution of the electrons to the pulse is in general smaller than the contribution of the positive ions, because the ionization by collision takes place usually at a distance from the wire smaller than the radius of the wire.

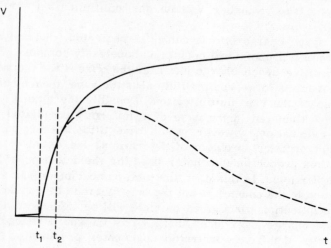

Fig. 4.1 — Schematic representation of the shape of the pulse of a proportional counter.

When all the primary ions are not produced at the same place, but are distributed along a track of finite length, the electrons from the various sections of the track will reach the gas-multiplication region at various times. This modifies the shape of the initial part of the pulse in a manner that depends on the position and orientation of the track. But the shape of the pulse after a time much longer than the time for collection of electrons will not be appreciably affected. Moreover, as long as space-charge effects can be neglected, the pulse shape for a given gas multiplication will be independent of the number of primary ions.

Usually the time constant RC or, more generally, the resolving time of the amplifier is chosen large compared with the time t_2 for the collection of electrons, but short compared with the total time for the collection of positive ions. The observed pulse shape will then be of the type represented by the dotted line in Fig. 4.1. The pulse height will depend somewhat on the value of the resolving time but will be independent of the position of the track because the latter affects the shape of only the initial part of the pulse.

Again under the assumption that space-charge effects can be neglected, the time dependence of the current through the counter when a
continuous source of ionization is suddenly turned on or off is identical to the time dependence of the voltage of the wire when a number
of ion pairs is produced simultaneously in the counter, as in the case
of an ionization chamber without gas multiplication (see Chap. 3,
Sec. 3.4).

When space-charge effects cannot be neglected, the analysis of the
operation of a proportional counter is hopelessly complex. The effect
of the positive space charge left near the wire after the removal of
the electrons is to weaken the field near the wire, thereby decreasing
the value of the gas multiplication. Possibly the size of the effect
could be calculated in the case of a uniformly irradiated chamber.
Such a calculation, however, would have little bearing on the more
important practical problem of determining the effect of the space
charge in a proportional counter used for the detection of individual
ionizing particles. In this case, the total number of ion pairs produced
per second in the counter is not the only factor to be considered. The
gas multiplication for a given particle will be influenced not only by
the space charge it produces, but also by the space charge produced
by particles that have penetrated the counter previously. These two
effects require separate investigation. The first effect will depend,
for one thing, on the orientation of the track, because this determines
both the length of the wire over which the space charge is distributed
and the time interval during which the space charge is produced.

It does not seem practical to predict theoretically the conditions
under which space-charge effects start to become noticeable, nor to
describe accurately the operation of proportional counters when this
occurs. Whenever proportional counters are to be used for quantitative measurements, it is advisable to test their operation by checking
the uniformity of the pulses produced by particles dissipating a given
amount of energy in the counter. A further test is to determine
whether or not the gas multiplication is independent of the primary
ionization.

4.2 Experimental Values of the Gas Multiplication for Various
Gases. It has been shown in the preceding section that, when it is
sufficiently small, the gas multiplication M for a given gas is a function of only the two variables $V_0/\ln(b/a)$ and pa. From this fact it is
possible to calculate M for any set of values of V_0, p, a, and b if M
has been measured as a function of V_0 and p with a given counter
(a and b constant).

Measurements of the gas multiplication as a function of voltage and
pressure were carried out for a number of gases. Alpha particles

from a polonium source were introduced in the counter, and the pulses, after suitable amplification, were observed on the screen of an oscilloscope. Then the voltage across the counter was reduced until the counter was operating as an ionization chamber without gas multiplication, and the gain of the amplifier was increased until the output pulses had again the same amplitude. The increase in the gain of the amplifier was taken as a measure of the gas multiplication. This procedure would be rigorously correct only if the resolving time of the amplifier was large compared with the duration of the pulses. Actually, the resolving time was approximately 100 μsec, which is long compared with the time for the collection of electrons but short compared with the time for the collection of positive ions. The error thus introduced is not, however, very serious, for when the counter is used without gas multiplication the pulse is due mainly to the motion of the electrons (Chap. 3, Sec. 3.6), and when it is used with gas multiplication the main part of the voltage change caused by the motion of the positive ions takes place in a time much less than 100 μsec. Moreover, this error does not affect the relative values of M because the pulse shape of a proportional counter does not change appreciably with gas multiplication.

Some of the gases investigated are listed below, along with references to the figures which summarize the experimental results. It must be emphasized that no effort was made to reach any high degree of accuracy in obtaining the experimental data presented here.

Fig. 4.2	Tank hydrogen
Fig. 4.3	Methane
Figs. 4.4 and 4.5	Tank argon
Fig. 4.6	Spectroscopic nitrogen
Fig. 4.7	Boron trifluoride
Fig. 4.8	90% hydrogen$-$10% methane mixture
Fig. 4.9	98% argon$-$2% CO_2 mixture
Fig. 4.10	90% argon$-$10% CO_2 mixture
Fig. 4.11	84% argon$-$16% propane mixture

From an examination of the experimental results summarized in Figs. 4.2 to 4.11, one can draw the following conclusions:

1. In most cases, the gas multiplication is, over a wide region, an approximately exponential function of the voltage.

2. The slope of the curve which represents ln M as a function of V_0 increases with decreasing pressure and decreasing wire diameter. For low pressures of hydrogen, argon, or nitrogen, the gas multiplication changes so rapidly with voltage that the counter is difficult to

use. The addition of a small amount of carbon dioxide to argon or of methane to hydrogen makes the dependence of M on V_0 at low pressures much less critical.

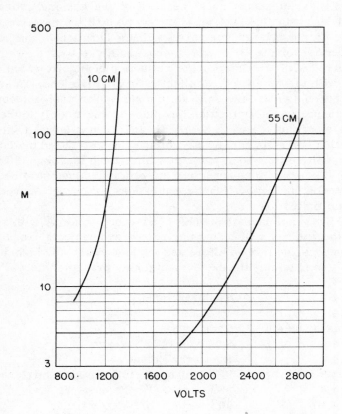

Fig. 4.2—Tank hydrogen, 99.97 per cent pure. Wire diameter 2a = 0.010 in.; cylinder diameter 2b = 0.87 in. Gas multiplication M vs. voltage for pressures of 10 and 55 cm Hg.

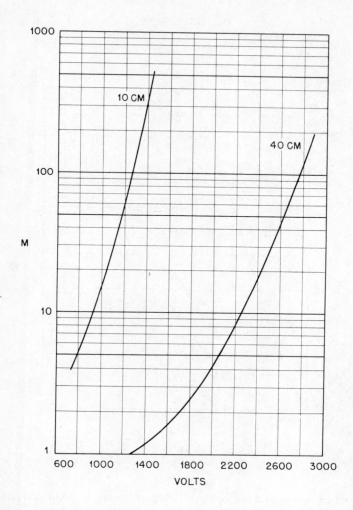

Fig. 4.3 —Methane, 85 per cent pure. Wire diameter 2a = 0.010 in.; cylinder diameter 2b = 0.87 in. Gas multiplication M vs. voltage for pressures of 10 and 40 cm Hg.

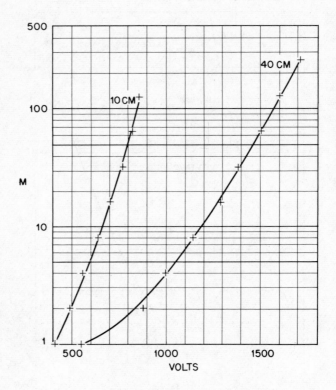

Fig. 4.4—Tank argon, 99.6 per cent pure. Wire diameter 2a = 0.01 in.; cylinder diameter 2b = 0.87 in. Gas multiplication M vs. voltage for pressures of 10 and 40 cm Hg.

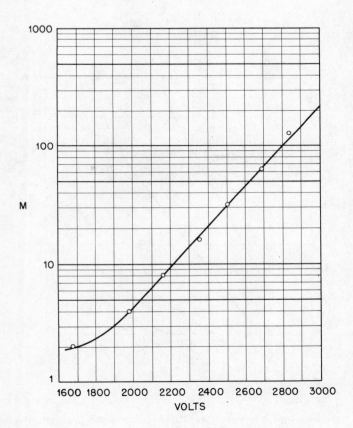

Fig. 4.5—Tank argon, 99.6 per cent pure. Wire diameter 0.001 in.; cylinder diameter 1.56 in. Gas multiplication M vs. voltage for a pressure of 6.8 atm.

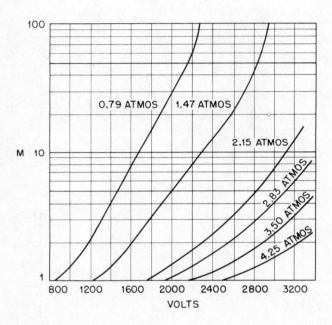

Fig. 4.6 — Spectroscopic nitrogen. Wire diameter 2a = 0.001 in.; cylinder diameter 1.56 in. Gas multiplication M vs. voltage for pressures from 0.79 to 4.25 atm.

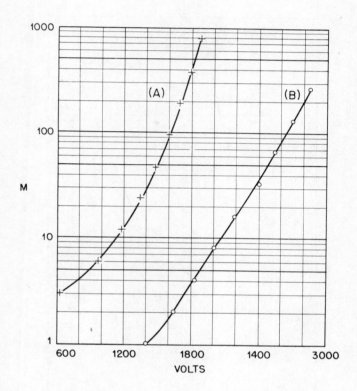

Fig. 4.7—Boron trifluoride. Gas multiplication M vs. voltage. (A) Wire diameter 2a = 0.010 in.; cylinder diameter 2b = 1.50 in.; pressure p = 10 cm Hg. (B) Wire diameter 2a = 0.001 in.; cylinder diameter, 1.56 in.; pressure p = 80.4 cm Hg.

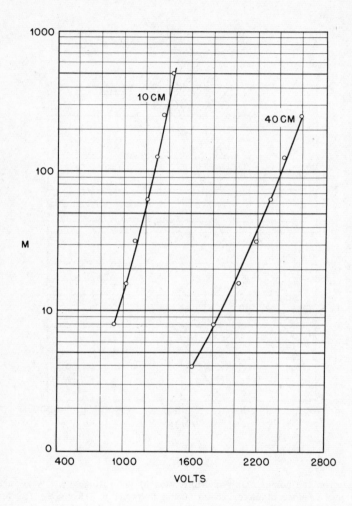

Fig. 4.8—Mixture of 90 per cent hydrogen and 10 per cent methane. Wire diameter 2a = 0.10 in.; cylinder diameter 2b = 0.87 in. Gas multiplication M vs. voltage for pressures of 10 and 40 cm Hg.

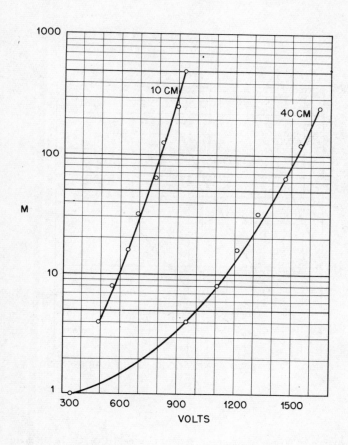

Fig. 4.9—Mixture of 98 per cent argon and 2 per cent CO_2. Wire diameter 2a = 0.10 in.; cylinder diameter 2b = 0.87 in. Gas multiplication M vs. voltage for pressures of 10 and 40 cm Hg.

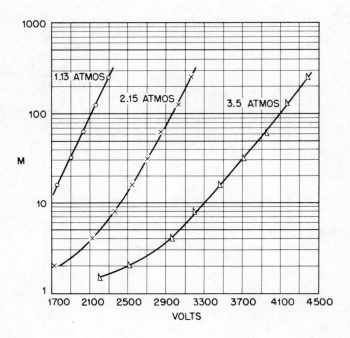

Fig. 4.10—Mixture of 90 per cent argon and 10 per cent CO_2. Wire diameter 2a = 0.005 in.; cylinder diameter 2b = 1.56 in. Gas multiplication M vs. voltage for pressures of 1.13, 2.15, and 3.5 atm.

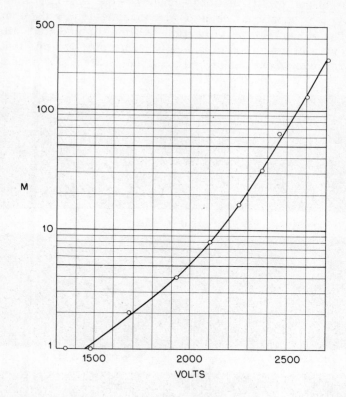

Fig. 4.11—Mixture of 84 per cent argon and 16 per cent propane. Wire diameter 2a = 0.001 in.; cylinder diameter 2b = 1.56 in. Gas multiplication M vs. voltage at a pressure of 6.83 atm.

An effort was made to verify experimentally the relation expressed in Eq. 2 by comparing the curves of V_0 vs. p at constant M with argon-filled counters of different dimensions, namely, 2a = 0.010 in.; 2b = 0.87 in.; 2a = 0.001 in., 2b = 1.56 in.; 2a = 0.002 in., 2b = 1.56 in.; 2a = 0.005 in., 2b = 1.56 in. Discrepancies of the order of 10 per cent were found between the values of V_0 observed with a given counter and those computed by means of Eq. 2 from the results obtained with a counter of different dimensions. It is difficult to decide whether or not the observed discrepancies are significant. They may well be due to errors in measurement of the wire diameter.

4.3   The Shape of Proportional-counter Pulses. The shape of
pulses from a proportional counter was investigated by determining
the intensity of current as a function of time immediately after a
constant source of ionization is suddenly turned off. For this test, the
pulsed x-ray equipment described in Chap. 3, Sec. 3.8 was used.

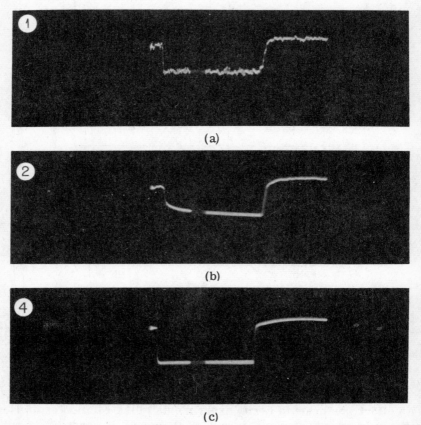

Fig. 4.12 — Photographic records of pulses of a cylindrical chamber upon sudden interruption of constant source of ionization. (a) Without gas multiplication. (b) With gas
multiplication. (c) Calibration pulse. The gain for (b) and (c) was about one-thirtieth
that for (a). The total duration of the sweep was 67 μsec.

The counter had an inner diameter of 0.75 in. The wire was 0.010 in.
in diameter and 6 in. in length. The x-ray beam was admitted into the
counter through a thin brass window. The irradiated section of the
counter was 1.5 in. in length. The counter was connected in the same
way as the ionization chamber shown in Chap. 3, Fig. 3.11. The resolving time of the amplifier was 0.8 μsec.

Some of the results obtained with a gas filling of 30 cm Hg of argon and CO_2 (98 per cent argon and 2 per cent CO_2) are shown by photographic records reproduced in Fig. 4.12. The length of the sweep was 67 μsec. Trace (a) was obtained with 300 volts across the counter, at which voltage no gas multiplication occurs. Under these conditions,

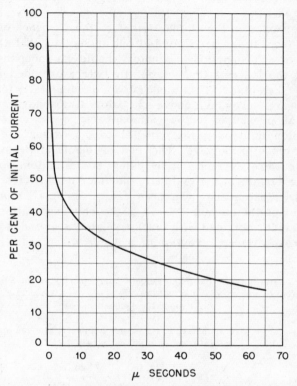

Fig. 4.13 — Current as a function of time in a proportional counter upon sudden interruption of a constant source of ionization [from trace (b), Fig. 4.12].

the current through the counter was 1.3×10^{-8} amp. Trace (b) was obtained with 1,600 volts across the counter, at which voltage the gas multiplication was about 30, giving a current through the counter of 6.5×10^{-7} amp. Trace (c) represents a calibration pulse obtained by sending through the leak resistor of the counter a current equal to 6.5×10^{-7} amp and then cutting it off electronically (Chap. 3, Sec. 3.8). The gain of the amplifier was of course much lower for the traces (b) and (c) than it was for trace (a). Figure 4.13 gives the current as a function of time, as obtained from the counter pulse shown in trace (b) of Fig. 4.12 and from the calibration pulse shown in trace (c). It will be seen that the shape of the pulse exhibits the features that may be expected from a qualitative analysis of the operation of the counter, as discussed in Sec. 4.1.

Experiments were carried out with different values of x-ray intensity at pressures from 20 to 76 cm Hg, and with values of the multiplication from 20 to 300. No large differences in the pulse shapes were detected.

4.4 Dependence of the Pulse Height on the Distance of the Track from the Wire. It has been pointed out in Sec. 4.1 that the height of the pulses of a proportional counter should be independent of the distance of the ionizing track from the wire, provided no electron attachment takes place. This was tested experimentally for a number of gases, at pressures both above and below atmospheric. The measurements at pressures below atmospheric were carried out by shooting polonium α particles parallel to the axis and close to the cylinder or close to the wire. The measurements at pressures above atmospheric were carried out by using two polonium sources, one on the inner surface of the cylinder, the other on the wire. The range of the α particles, at the pressures used, was small compared with the diameter of the counter. Some of the observed ratios ρ between the pulse heights obtained with tracks located near the wall and near the wire, respectively, are listed in Table 4.1 along with the data

Table 4.1 — Ratio Between the Pulse Heights Corresponding to the Same Primary Ionization Produced Near the Wall and Near the Wire, Respectively, in a Proportional Counter

(p = pressure, 2a = wire diameter, 2b = cylinder diameter, M = gas multiplication, ρ = ratio between the pulse heights)

Gas	p	2a, in.	2b, in.	M	ρ
H_2	22 cm Hg	0.010	1.5	250	1.0
A (99.6 % pure)	6.8 atm	0.001	1.56	128	1.0
CH_4	22 cm Hg	0.010	1.5	57	1.0
BF_3	10 cm Hg	0.010	1.5	80	1.0
BF_3	1.05 atm	0.001	1.56	128	~0.02
BF_3	1.05 atm	0.001	1.56	1000	0.1
84% argon and 16% propane (commercial)	6.8 atm	0.001	1.56	128	0.2

describing the experimental conditions under which the measurements were taken. The value $\rho = 1$ found for these ratios in the case of argon and hydrogen is in agreement with the fact already mentioned that no appreciable attachment takes place in these gases (see Chap. 1, Sec. 1.4). Hydrogen, however, was tested only at low pressure. For BF_3, $\rho = 1$ when a low pressure and a comparatively thick wire are used, whereas $\rho \ll 1$ when a high pressure and a compartively thin wire are used. This behavior is explained by the following considerations: (1) for BF_3 the electron attachment decreases with increasing E/p, while for a given value of E/p, it is proportional to the pressure; (2) the field strength near the cylinder wall, for a given gas multiplication, is weaker the thinner the wire.

4.5 <u>End Effects; Eccentricity of the Wire.</u> The central wire of a proportional counter is often connected at each end to a metal rod sufficiently thicker than the wire itself so that no gas multiplication takes place at the rod's surface. The supports of the wire are in this

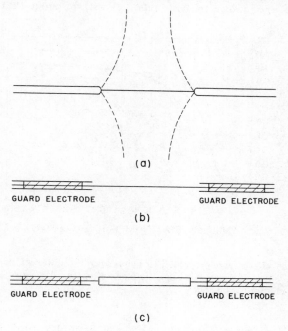

(a)

GUARD ELECTRODE   GUARD ELECTRODE

(b)

GUARD ELECTRODE   GUARD ELECTRODE

(c)

Fig. 4.14—Different ways of supporting the central wire in a proportional counter. Shaded areas represent insulators.

case a part of the collecting electrode [see Fig. 4.14(a)]. In some counters, the wire is supported by and insulated from two metal tubes which form guard electrodes [see Fig. 4.14 (b)]. In both cases, the electric field near the ends of the wire is different from the field

near the center. The modification of the field has two separate effects. The lines of force near the ends of the wire are not radial, so
that the "sensitive volume" is not a rectangular cylinder, but has
roughly the shape shown in Fig. 4.14(a). "Sensitive volume" means
here the region where electrons are produced that give rise to gas
multiplication. The field strength at the surface of the wire is weaker
near the ends and reaches its normal value only at some distance
from the ends. This causes the gas multiplication to decrease gradually toward either end of the wire.

The end effects were investigated by shooting α particles in a direction perpendicular to the wire, at various distances from the ends
of the wire. The wire was 0.010 in. in diameter, and the supporting
rods were 0.025 in. in diameter in one case, 0.040 in. in another case.
The results are shown in Fig. 4.15. It will be seen that the normal

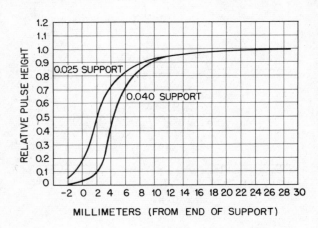

Fig. 4.15 — End effects in a proportional counter for two different thicknesses of the
wire support. Wire diameter 0.010 in.; cylinder diameter 0.87 in.; gas filling 22 cm
Hg of H_2; gas multiplication 250.

gas multiplication is reached only at a considerable distance from
the ends of the wire, a distance that increases with the thickness of
the supporting rods. On the other hand, if the supporting rods are
part of the collecting electrode, they must not be made too thin, or
gas multiplication will take place at their surfaces. (In the measurements mentioned above, when 0.025-in.-diameter supporting rods
were used and the gas multiplication at the wire was 250, a gas multiplication of about 10 was observed at the rods.)

The end effects may be avoided by supporting the collecting wire by means of guard electrodes of the same diameter as the wire, as indicated in Fig. 4.14(c). A counter designed according to this principle will be described in Chap. 7, Sec. 7.15.

It has been implicitly assumed so far that the two electrodes of a proportional counter are exactly coaxial cylinders. The effect of a small eccentricity of the wire will now be investigated. For this purpose, assume that the inner and outer electrodes are cylinders with their axes parallel but not coincident. The problem of determining the electric field between the two cylinders may be solved by considering the field produced by two straight parallel filaments of infinite length, uniformly charged with equal and opposite linear densities of charge. If λ and $-\lambda$ are the densities of charge, and r_1 and r_2 are the distances of a point P from the positive and the negative filaments, respectively, the potential at the point P can be expressed as

$$V = 2\lambda \ (\ln m) + k \tag{3}$$

where $m = r_2/r_1$ and k is a constant.

It can be shown easily that the equipotential surface corresponding to a given value of the voltage V and therefore of the parameter m is a circular cylinder of radius

$$r = d \ \frac{m}{m^2 - 1} \tag{4}$$

the axis of which is in the plane of the two filaments at a distance

$$\delta = \frac{d}{m^2 - 1} \tag{5}$$

from the positive filament. In the above equations, d indicates the distance between the two filaments.

Suppose now that the counter is formed by two cylinders of radii a and b respectively, the axes of which are at a distance Δ apart. The field between the two cylinders will be identical to the field produced by two straight filaments arranged in such a way that the surfaces of the two electrodes are equipotential surfaces (see Fig. 4.16).

The distance d between the two filaments and the values m_a and m_b of the parameter m at the surface of the electrodes are determined by the equations

$$a = d \; \frac{m_a}{m_a^2 - 1}$$

$$b = d \; \frac{m_b}{m_b^2 - 1} \tag{6}$$

$$\Delta = \delta_b - \delta_a = d \left[\frac{1}{m_b^2 - 1} - \frac{1}{m_a^2 - 1} \right]$$

The potential V in the space between the two cylinders is given by Eq. 3 where the constants λ and k are determined by the boundary conditions.

$$V = 0 \qquad \text{for} \quad m = m_a \quad \text{(i.e., at the surface of the inner electrode)}$$

$$V = - V_0 \quad \text{for} \quad m = m_b \quad \text{(i.e., at the surface of the outer electrode)}$$

Thus

$$V = - V_0 \; \frac{\ln (m/m_a)}{\ln (m_b/m_a)} \tag{7}$$

The electric field strength $\vec{E}$ is computed as the negative gradient of V.

$$\vec{E} = \frac{V_0}{\ln (m_b/m_a)} \; \text{grad} \, (\ln m) \tag{8}$$

As an example, the magnitude of E can be calculated for points of the plane which contain the axes of the two cylinders as well as the two fictitious line charges. In this plane the following relation holds:

$$m = \frac{r_2}{r_1} = \frac{d \pm r_1}{r_1}$$

where the plus sign refers to points of the plane for which $r_2 > d$, and the minus sign to points of the plane for which $r_2 < d$. From Eq. 8 it follows

$$\vec{E} = \frac{V_0}{\ln (m_b/m_a)} \frac{d}{r_1(d \pm r_1)} \tag{9}$$

If the above equation is applied to points at the surface of the inner electrode ($r_1 = a - \delta_a$, $r_1 = a + \delta_a$), the values of the maximum and minimum field strengths at the surface of this electrode are obtained. These values are given by

$$E_{max} = \frac{V_0}{\ln (m_b/m_a)} \frac{d}{(a - \delta_a)(d - a + \delta_a)}$$

$$E_{min} = \frac{V_0}{\ln (m_b/m_a)} \frac{d}{(a + \delta_a)(d + a + \delta_a)} \tag{10}$$

Now assume that the eccentricity of the wire is small. Since d becomes infinity and δ_a becomes zero when the eccentricity vanishes, we can assume that $d \gg a$ and $\delta_a \ll a$. The maximum relative variation of the field at the surface of the inner electrode as given by Eq. 10 may then be written as

$$\frac{\delta E}{E} = 2 \left(\frac{\delta_a}{a} + \frac{a}{d} \right) \tag{11}$$

If $b \gg a$ and the eccentricity is assumed to be small, Eqs. 11 and 6 yield

$$\frac{\delta E}{E} = 4 \frac{a\Delta}{b^2} \tag{11a}$$

From this equation and from the experimentally determined dependence of the gas multiplication on electric-field strength at the inner electrode, it is easy to determine the spread in gas multiplication caused by a given eccentricity of the wire. For instance, in the case of a 1-in. counter (2b = 1 in.) with a 0.010-in. wire (2a = 0.010 in.) 0.010 in. off center (Δ = 0.010 in.), Eq. 11a yields $\delta E/E = 8 \times 10^{-4}$. If the counter is filled with hydrogen at 55 cm pressure and operated at a gas multiplication of about 100, such a variation of the electric-field

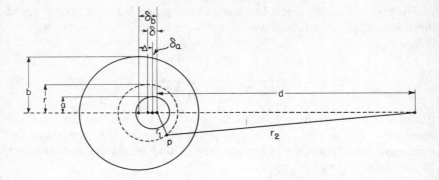

Fig. 4.16 — Diagram for the calculation of the field in a counter with eccentric wire.

strength will produce a change in gas multiplication of the order of 1 per cent.

4.6 <u>Spread in Pulse Height</u>.　There are several reasons why tracks producing the same amount of ionization in the sensitive volume of a proportional counter may fail to give rise to pulses of equal height. Some of these reasons have already been mentioned: space-charge effects (Sec. 4.1), electron attachment (Sec. 4.4), end effects (Sec. 4.5), and eccentricity of the wire (Sec. 4.5). Other possible causes of spread in pulse height are inequalities in the diameter of the wire and the presence of dust particles on the wire. These are likely to be particularly troublesome if a very thin wire is used, and a thin wire is necessary in order to keep the operating voltage within reasonable limits when the gas pressure in the counter is high. With an actual counter (2a = 0.001 in., 2b = 1.56 in., gas filling 6.8 atm of an argon-propane mixture, polonium source on the wire), a spread in the pulse height of the order of 50 per cent was observed before the wire was cleaned. After the wire had been carefully cleaned, the spread in pulse height was reduced to about 10 per cent.

A typical pulse-height-distribution curve is shown in Fig. 4.17. Similar curves were obtained with reasonably monoenergetic sources of α particles whenever carefully cleaned counters were used and care was taken to avoid the disturbing influence of end effects or electron capture. Under these conditions, the width of the pulse-height distribution (defined as the pulse-height interval that contains 50 per cent of all the observed pulses) was found to be between 5 and 10 per cent of the average pulse height. This represents an upper limit for the spread inherent in the gas multiplication, because it is likely that at least part of the observed spread may be caused by lack of monochromaticity of the sources used.

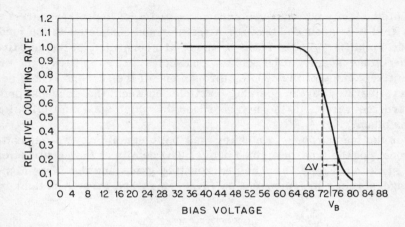

Fig. 4.17—Typical spread in pulse height for a proportional counter. Wire diameter 0.010 in.; cylinder diameter 1.5 in.; gas filling 39 cm Hg of H_2 plus 4 cm Hg of CH_4; gas multiplication 620. The experiment was performed by shooting a collimated beam of α particles through the counter, in a direction perpendicular to the axis. The output pulses of the amplifier were analyzed by means of an electronic discriminator. The curve gives number of pulses against bias voltage. The width of the pulse-height distribution is $\Delta V/V_b = 0.06$.

4.7   Multiple-wire Counter. A proportional counter, in which a grid formed by a number of parallel and equidistant wires takes the place of the single wire used in the conventional counters, was developed at the Los Alamos Laboratories. The diagram of such a counter is schematically represented in Fig. 4.18. The grid W is

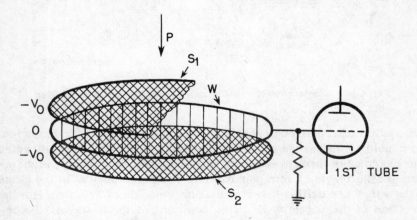

Fig. 4.18—Schematic diagram of a multiple-wire proportional counter. S_1 and S_2 form the high-voltage electrode; W is the collecting electrode. The arrow P represents the direction of the beam of ionizing particles.

mounted rigidly between two screens S_1 and S_2 of high transparency. The grid W is grounded through a resistor and connected to the input of the amplifier. The screens S_1 and S_2 are connected to the negative high-voltage supply. The ionizing particles are admitted into the sensitive volume of the counter through one of the screens. The electrons liberated by an ionizing particle between the screens drift toward the wires, in the neighborhood of which gas multiplication takes place.

For testing purposes a counter was built containing two separate elements of the type described above. The details of the construction are shown in Fig. 4.19. The two counting grids and the three high-voltage screens are mounted on invar rings and stretched tight by

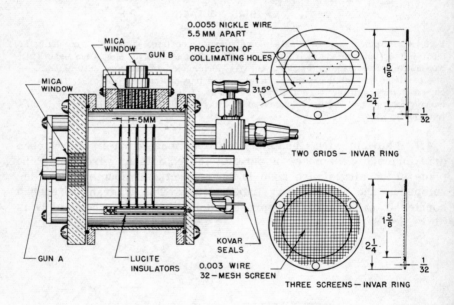

Fig. 4.19—Construction of a double multiple-wire proportional counter.

differential thermal contraction. Collimated beams of α particles, from polonium sources placed in the guns A and B, can be directed into the counter through either of two sets of holes (0.026 in. in diameter, 0.5 in. length, 2 mm separation). The holes normal to the plane of the wires are drilled in a row making an angle of 31.5 deg with the direction of the wires so that five positions of the beam may be obtained between two neighboring wires. The counter was filled with a mixture of 97 per cent argon (99.6 per cent purity) and 3 per cent CO_2.

The resolving time of the amplifier used for the tests with the counter described above was about 100 μsec.

The gas multiplication as a function of voltage was measured at pressures of 4 and 30 cm Hg. The results are presented in Fig. 4.20.

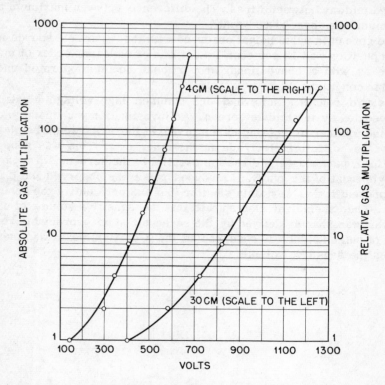

Fig. 4.20—Gas multiplication M vs. voltage for the multiple-wire proportional counter represented in Fig. 4.19; gas filling 97 per cent argon, 3 per cent CO_2 at total pressures of 4 cm Hg and 30 cm Hg. The gas multiplication for the lower pressure is plotted on an arbitrary scale.

At 30 cm Hg pressure the measurements were carried out, as described in Sec. 4.2, by comparison of pulse heights with and without gas multiplication. At 4 cm pressure, the primary ionization in the counter was too small to permit observation of ionization pulses without gas multiplication, so that the gas multiplication is plotted on an arbitrary scale (by taking M = 1 for the lowest gas multiplication which gave measurable pulses).

The variation of the pulse height with the distance of the track from the counting wires was investigated by shooting α particles perpendicularly to the plane of the wires through the holes in front of the gun A. A continuous and periodic variation of pulse height was observed as the α-particle beam was displaced with respect to the wires. The pulse height reached a maximum when the α particles passed near one of the wires and a minimum when the α particles passed midway between wires. The difference between maximum and minimum was about 11 per cent.

The spread in pulse height observed with the α-particle source in a given position was 13 per cent, i.e., it was of the same order of magnitude as with a conventional proportional counter operated under similar conditions.

The two counting units had one common high-voltage electrode represented by the middle screen. An investigation was made to determine whether or not the pulses in one of the units would be picked up by the collecting electrode in the other unit. This was done by shooting α particles in a direction parallel to the screens, through the holes in front of the gun B. No induced pulse was observed and if any was present it was certainly smaller than 0.2 per cent of the genuine pulse. The experiment also showed that the sensitive volume of each counter was sharply defined by the screens and no appreciable variation of pulse height was observed as the α-particle beam was moved across the sensitive volume.

Chapter 5

BETA-RAY, GAMMA-RAY, AND X-RAY DETECTORS

5.1 General Considerations. All the instruments described in this chapter are essentially detectors of high-energy electrons. Gamma and x rays (both referred to in what follows as "γ rays") act upon the detector through the agency of secondary electrons generated in the walls or in the gas of the chamber.

Unless a very high pressure is used, individual electrons, because of their small specific ionization, produce only a small number of ions in a chamber. For this reason the electron detectors used in the Los Alamos Project were limited to two categories: (1) discharge counters (Geiger-Mueller counters) in which the primary ionization produced by the electron is used to initiate an avalanche; (2) integrating chambers in which the ionization current produced by a large number of electrons is recorded.

Because of the small range of electrons in solid matter, β-ray detectors must have very thin walls or be provided with thin windows, unless the source is placed inside the counter.

Gamma-ray detectors generally have walls of a thickness greater than the maximum range of the secondary electrons, yet not so thick as to produce any appreciable attenuation of the primary γ radiation.

5.2 Yield of γ-ray Counters. With regard to its response, a discharge counter may be assumed to record all electrons that traverse its sensitive volume, at least if the pressure is sufficiently high and the counting rate sufficiently low. Thus these counters have practically 100 per cent detection efficiency for β rays. For γ rays, the counting yield η of a discharge counter, defined as the ratio of the number of counts to the number of photons traversing the counter, is given by the probability that at least one secondary electron will be produced in the wall by a photon and will emerge from the wall into the sensitive volume of the counter. (Production of secondary electrons in the gas can usually be neglected.) The thickness of the effective layer, i.e., the layer from which secondary electrons may emerge into the counter, increases with the "range" of the electrons. The number of electrons produced in this layer is proportional to its thickness and to the cross section for production of electrons by γ rays in the wall material. The angle of incidence θ of the photons upon the wall will not affect the yield if the secondary electrons proceed in the direction of the incoming photons. This is so because the thickness of the effective layer is proportional to cos θ, while the path of the photons in this layer is proportional to 1 cos θ. In the opposite limiting case, i.e., when the electrons are completely scattered so as to be isotropically distributed, the yield will be proportional to $1/\cos \theta$. This is so because the thickness of the effective layer, in this case, is independent of θ, while the path of the photon in this layer is proportional to $1/\cos \theta$. A semiempirical expression for the yield η was derived under the assumption of complete scattering, a condition that is fairly well verified for elements of high atomic number and for comparatively small electron energies (Metallurgical Laboratory report). For perpendicular incidence

$$\eta = 0.135(\mu_{ph} R_{ph} + \mu_c R_c + 2\mu_{pr} R_{pr} \qquad (1)$$

where μ_{ph}, μ_c, and μ_{pr} are the absorption coefficients of γ rays in the wall material relative to photo effect, Compton effect, and pair production, respectively, and R_{ph}, and R_c, and R_{pr} are the extrapolated ranges of monokinetic electrons whose energies correspond to the mean energies of the secondary electrons for the three respective processes. The factor 2, which multiplies the last term, corresponds to the production of two secondary electrons when a photon undergoes materialization. The numerical factor 0.135 is chosen empirically for the best fit with the experimental results.

With the assumption of complete scattering, the number of electrons emerging from a given surface is independent of the orientation of this surface in the γ-ray beam. Hence the yield of a counter of any shape can be calculated by multiplying the expression for η given in Eq. 1 by the ratio of the total wall area to the cross-sectional area of the counter perpendicular to the direction of the γ-ray beam. For a cylindrical counter with its axis perpendicular to the direction of incidence, this factor is π. Figure 5.1 gives the calculated yield as a function of energy for a cylindrical counter with copper and bismuth walls under the conditions specified above. The behavior indicated by these curves was checked experimentally by W. C. Peacock.[*]

* Massachusetts Institute of Technology Thesis, 1944.

Admittedly, the assumption of complete scattering is very crude and the reason that it leads to results in fairly good agreement with the experimental facts is that it does not enter critically in the computation of the yield of a counter if the walls, from which secondary electrons are emitted, present all possible orientations to the incident γ rays, as they do in most practical cases.

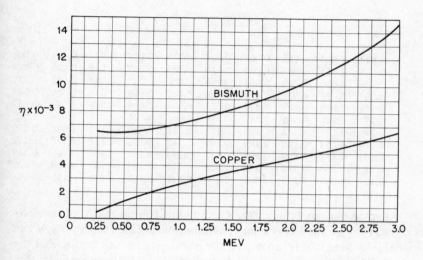

Fig. 5.1 — Counting yield η of cylindrical counters with bismuth and copper walls as a function of γ-ray energy.

The variation of η with energy and with atomic number, as represented by Fig. 5.1, is made clear, at least qualitatively, by the dependence of the μ's and the R's on the above two quantities.

A completely theoretical determination of the yield for a parallel-plate lead counter was attempted at Los Alamos. These calculations apply to energies higher than those at which Eq. 1 may be expected to hold. Some simplifying assumptions were made concerning the energy distribution of the secondary electrons arising from the various processes. It was assumed, moreover, that all secondary electrons are produced in the forward direction. The energy loss of electrons by ionization and radiation, as well as their scattering, was taken into account. Pair production by the secondary photons was neglected. The results are summarized in Table 5.1, which gives the average number of electrons emerging from a lead plate of a given thickness when a photon of a given energy falls perpendicularly upon it. Where this number is small compared with 1, it also represents the yield η defined as the probability of at least one electron emerging from the plate per incident photon.

Table 5.1 — Average Number of Electrons Emerging from a Lead Plate When a Photon Falls Perpendicularly upon the Plate

Photon energy, mev	Lead thickness, cm									
	0.1	0.2	0.3	0.4	0.5	0.6	0.7	0.8	0.9	1.0
5	0.027	0.030	0.028	0.027	0.027	0.025	0.025	0.023	0.021	0.021
6	0.036	0.043	0.041	0.039	0.038	0.035	0.033	0.032	0.029	0.027
7	0.048	0.058	0.059	0.054	0.052	0.050	0.045	0.042	0.042	0.037
8	0.057	0.072	0.071	0.068	0.064	0.061	0.059	0.055	0.052	0.047
9	0.065	0.088	0.089	0.084	0.079	0.074	0.069	0.066	0.062	0.057
10	0.075	0.102	0.106	0.101	0.096	0.088	0.085	0.079	0.074	0.070
12	0.088	0.129	0.141	0.136	0.127	0.121	0.112	0.105	0.097	0.090
14	0.100	0.150	0.170	0.169	0.161	0.149	0.139	0.129	0.120	0.112
16	0.109	0.172	0.200	0.203	0.195	0.182	0.168	0.156	0.145	0.136
18	0.117	0.189	0.226	0.236	0.228	0.214	0.198	0.183	0.169	0.157
20	0.124	0.205	0.249	0.264	0.259	0.245	0.226	0.209	0.193	0.178

5.3 Response of an Integrating Chamber. The intensity of the ionization current in an integrating chamber irradiated with γ rays can be calculated accurately only for the case where the walls and the gas of the chamber have nearly the same atomic number. In this case, the ionization of the gas in the sensitive volume of the chamber is the same as if the gas were surrounded by more gas of the same nature rather than by the chamber's walls. The whole energy E of a photon that undergoes an absorption or a scattering process goes into secondary electrons or into photons of low energy. It is eventually dissipated over a distance short compared with the mean free path of the primary photon, thereby producing E/W_0 ion pairs, where W_0 is the energy per ion pair. Hence, a γ-ray flux of n photons per sq cm will produce a number $n\mu(E/W_0)$ of ion pairs per cu cm of the gas, where μ is the total absorption coefficient of photons in the gas. The ionization current in the chamber, which is assumed to be uniformly irradiated throughout its volume, will then be given by

$$I = en\mu \frac{E}{W_0} A \tag{2}$$

where e is the charge of the electron and A the volume of the chamber. If e is measured in electrostatic units, the quantity $e\mu(E/W_0)$

represents the number of roentgens per incident photon produced in the gas of the chamber.

When the walls of the chamber are made of a material appreciably different in atomic number from the gas, the ionization cannot be calculated with Eq. 2. An approximate expression for the total number of ion pairs per second produced in the chamber is $N\eta\nu_{av}$, where N is the number of photons per second falling on the chamber, η is the yield as previously defined, and ν_{av} is the average number of ion pairs produced by each secondary electron in the chamber. The ionization current is then given by

$$I = eN\eta\nu_{av} \qquad (3)$$

The value of ν_{av} may be computed from the specific ionization of the secondary electrons and from their average path length in the chamber. In the computation of the latter quantity one must take into account the detour factor, i.e., the increase in path length caused by multiple scattering.* When the detour factor is small and when the pressure in the chamber is sufficiently low that the range of the secondary electrons is larger than the linear dimensions of the chamber, ν_{av} is practically indepedent of energy. Under these conditions the ionization current in the chamber shows the same dependence on the γ-ray energy as the yield η of a counter with the same wall material.

The response of an ionization chamber irradiated with a γ-ray source of variable intensity has been discussed in detail in Chap. 3, Sec. 3.4. It has been shown there that the total ionization current follows faithfully the variations of intensity of the ionizing radiation only if these variations are comparatively slow — or, more precisely, if the time during which an appreciable variation takes place is long compared with the time for collection of ions. In the case of variations that take place in times short compared with the time for collection of ions, only the electron current follows the changes of the ionizing radiation, while the intensity of the ion current remains practically constant.

Hence the chambers to be used for studying a rapidly varying γ radiation must be filled with a gas in which the electrons remain free. In order to avoid contamination of the gas, which may lead to electron attachment, sealing waxes and organic insulators must be avoided in the chamber construction.

---

* See, for instance, the article by W. Bothe in H. Geiger, "Handbuch der Physik," Vol. 22.2, pp. 26-28, Verlag Julius Springer, Berlin, 1933.

The relation between the observed output voltage and the number of ion pairs per second produced in the chamber is given in Eq. 26, Chap. 3.

$$V_e\,(t) = e\,\int_0^\infty\,N(t-t_1)\,X(t_1)\,dt_1 \tag{4}$$

where $X(t)$ represents the transient response of the detecting equipment including both the ionization chamber and the amplifier. This function can be determined by means of a pulsed x-ray source, as described in Chap. 3, Sec. 3.8.

5.4 Cylindrical γ-ray Ionization Chamber. Figure 5.2 represents a cylindrical γ-ray integrating ionization chamber 2 in. in diameter,

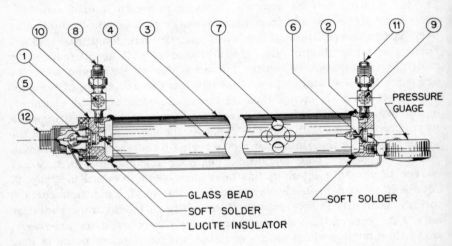

Fig. 5.2—Cylindrical γ-ray ionization chamber (see Sec. 5.4). 1 and 2, brass end pieces. 3, brass cylinder, 2 in. OD, $\frac{1}{32}$ in. wall thickness; this represents the high-voltage electrode. 4, Kovar wire, 0.025 in. in diameter; this represents the collecting electrode and has an active length of 29 in. 5 and 6, Kovar pieces supporting the collecting electrode by means of glass insulators; these pieces are grounded during operation of the chamber and act as guard electrodes. 7, circular holes, $\frac{1}{2}$ in. in diameter, covered with a 0.003-in. brass foil to admit x rays into the chamber for testing purposes. 8 and 11, couplings for connecting the chamber to the filling system. 9 and 10, needle valves. 12, male amphenol connector, insulated from the end pieces by a lucite plate. The pin of the connector is attached to the collecting electrode; the case is attached to the guard electrode (5) and to ground.

29 in. in effective length, which has proved very useful both in laboratory and in field work. The gas filling consists of an argon-CO_2 mixture (generally 96 per cent argon and 4 per cent CO_2) at a total

pressure of about 4.5 atm. It was found that a sufficient purity of the gas could be achieved by keeping the chamber under vacuum for approximately 12 hr, filling it with the appropriate argon-CO_2 mixture through a dry-ice trap, and then letting the gas circulate through a calcium purifier heated at 150°C for about 4 hr. It was found that this operation did not reduce the CO_2 content too much. The construction of the purifier used for this purpose, which is capable of handling eight chambers simultaneously, is shown in Fig. 5.3. Usually in the chambers thus prepared, no appreciable electron attachment can be detected even after several months. The volume of the chamber is 1,410 cu cm. The capacity of the collecting electrode is 12.7 $\mu\mu$f. The chamber is normally operated at −2,000 volts. Saturation is reached at about −400 volts and, with 1 g of radium at 1 m distance, the saturation current was found to be approximately 6×10^{-10} amp. The chamber was designed primarily for measuring rapid variations of the γ-ray intensity, but it was also widely used for static measurements.

For a cylindrical geometry and the condition that no negative ions are formed, the fraction of electron current is given by the equation (Chap. 3, Sec. 3.6.)

$$\frac{I_0^-}{I_0} = 1 - \frac{1}{2 \ln (b/a)} \tag{5}$$

where a is the radius of the inner electrode and b is the inner radius of the outer electrode. It is here assumed that $b \gg a$ and that the outer cylinder is kept at a negative potential with respect to the collecting electrode. For the chamber under consideration, Eq. 5 gives $I_0^-/I_0 = 0.886$.

Experiments were carried out to check the theoretical value of the electron current and also to determine the transient response of the ionization chamber. These experiments were performed with the pulsed x-ray source described in Chap. 3, Sec. 3.8, by observing the time dependence of the current subsequent to a sudden interruption of the x-ray beam. Measurements on many chambers of the type described gave values of I_0^-/I_0 that were usually within 1 or 2 per cent of the theoretical value, indicating the absence of any appreciable electron attachment.

The transient response of the chamber is illustrated in Fig. 5.4. The curve marked I^-/I_0 gives the calculated intensity of electron current in terms of the initial total current I_0 as a function of time, following a sudden interruption of the radiation. This curve was calculated under the assumption that the electrons in the chamber have

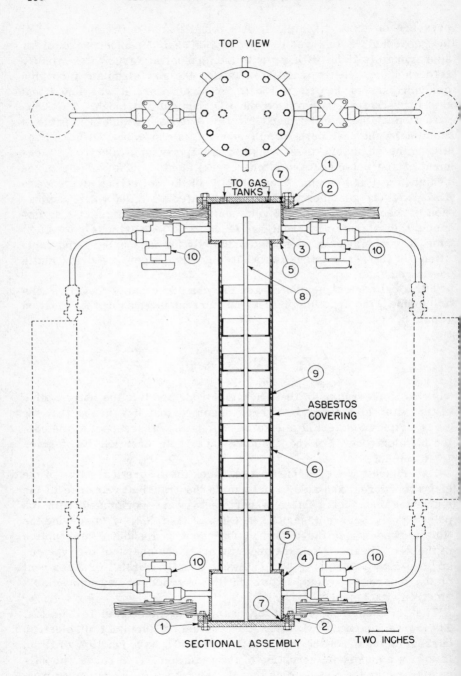

Fig. 5.3—See facing page for legend.

a constant drift velocity equal to 4×10^6 cm/sec. The curve marked I^+/I_0 gives the intensity of the positive ion current in terms of I_0 calculated by assuming a drift velocity proportional to the electric-field strength. The curve marked V/RI_0 gives the voltage drop across the leak resistor R in terms of RI_0 calculated by neglecting the contribution of the positive ion current, which can be considered as constant during the time of collection of the electrons. This curve was calculated by using a value of 0.48 μsec for the product RC of the resistance R and the capacity C of the collecting electrode and amplifier input. The amplifier was regarded as having infinite bandwidth. The crosses are experimental points taken from the oscilloscope trace. The agreement with the calculated curve is very satisfactory. It appears from Fig. 5.4 that the chamber described is capable of reproducing, without much distortion, variations of γ-ray intensity that take place in times of the order of several microseconds.

5.5 <u>Multiple-plate X-ray Ionization Chamber.</u> Figure 5.5 shows the construction of an ionization chamber that was used for measuring the time dependence of the intensity of very fast x-ray pulses. Only metal, porcelain, and glass are in contact with the gas. The seal between the bottom plate and the case is made gastight by means of a copper gasket. In order to increase the sensitivity, the electrode assembly consists of five circular aluminum disks connected alternately so that disks 2 and 4 form the collecting electrode, while disks 1, 3, and 5 form the high-voltage electrode. The gas filling consists of an argon-CO_2 mixture (90 per cent argon and 10 per cent CO_2) at a total pressure of 100 cm Hg. The gas is purified by circulation over hot calcium.

The chamber is normally operated at 2,000 volts. Under these conditions the drift velocity of electrons in the argon-CO_2 mixture is higher than 5×10^6 cm/sec. Since the separation of the electrodes is 1 cm, the resolving time of the chamber may be estimated to be less than 0.2 μsec. This chamber is thus considerably faster than the cylindrical chamber described in Sec. 5.4. This speed is due to the uniformly high field provided by the parallel-plate arrangement and to

---

Fig. 5.3—Hot calcium purifier. 1, steel end plate. 2, steel flange. 3 and 4, brass cylindrical sections, ⅛-in. wall. 5, brass rings, ¼ in. thick. 6, steel cylinder, ⅛-in. wall. 7, gasket made of 1⁄32-in. copper sheet. 8, ¼-in. steel rod. 9, brass baskets, provided with copper screens on the bottom and lined on the side with copper sheet. 10, packless valves. The heating element (about 300 watts power) is wound around the steel cylinder. The calcium, in the form of turnings, is placed in the baskets (9) by removing the end plate (1) and extracting the inner assembly formed by the steel rod (8) and the baskets (9). The connection to the pump is made by means of a 1-in. copper tube soldered to the brass cylinder (4). All joints are hard-soldered.

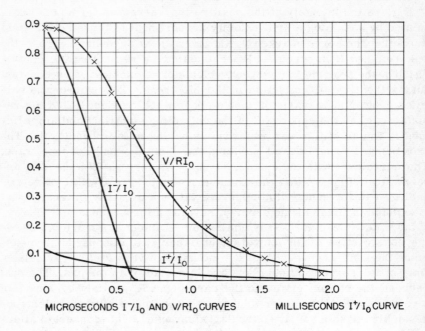

Fig. 5.4—Response of the cylindrical ionization chamber represented in Fig. 5.2 to a sudden interruption of a constant source of ionization. I^- = electron current (calculated). I^+ = positive ion current (calculated). I_0 = total initial current. V = voltage drop across the leak resistor R caused by the electron current (calculated for RC = 0.48 μsec). X = experimental values of V.

Fig. 5.5—Multiple-plate x-ray ionization chamber. 1, 3, and 5, dural disks, 1 mm thick, 3½ in. in diameter, forming the high-voltage electrode. They are connected by three threaded stems with brass spacers. These stems, of which two are shown in the drawing (6 and 7), are placed near the edge of the disks, at an angular distance of 120 deg. Two of the stems are supported by porcelain insulators (8), one by the center piece of a Kovar-glass seal (9), which provides electrical connection to the high-voltage electrode. Disks 1 and 3 have central holes ⅝ in. in diameter to permit the passage of the stem (10) supporting disks 2 and 4. 2 and 4, dural disks, 1 mm thick, 3½ in. in diameter, forming the collecting electrode. They are supported by a central threaded stem with brass spacer (10). This stem terminates in the center piece of a Kovar-glass seal (11), which provides electrical connection to the collecting electrode. The two disks have notches to avoid contacts with the stems supporting the disks 1, 3, and 5 (see detail 4). 12, steel cylinder, ³⁄₃₂-in. wall. 13, steel plate, ⅛ in. thick. 14, base steel plate ¼ in. thick, supporting the electrode assembly. 15, steel flange, ¼ in. thick. 16, connection for pressure gauge. 17, one of the two gas inlets.

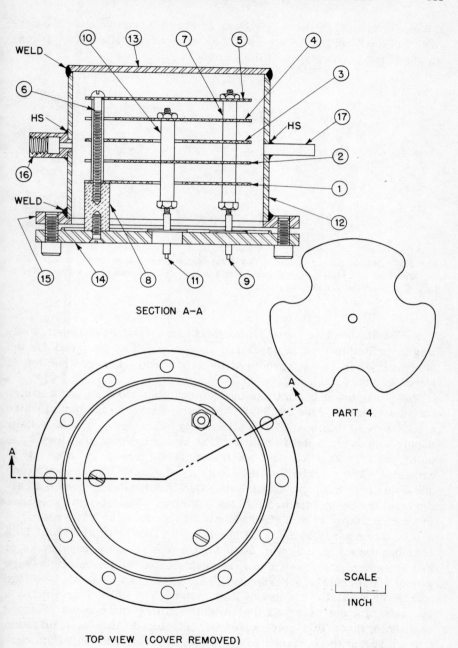

SECTION A—A

PART 4

SCALE
|—⊢—|
INCH

TOP VIEW (COVER REMOVED)

Fig. 5.5—See facing page for legend.

the small spacing of the electrodes. In Fig. 5.6 two oscilloscope records obtained with 370-kv x-ray pulses are reproduced as an example of the performance of the chamber.

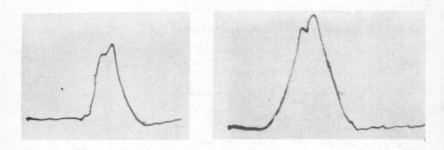

Fig. 5.6—Oscilloscope records of two x-ray pulses from a tube operated by a 370-kv Westinghouse impulse generator. Total duration of the sweeps 4.4 μsec. X-ray tube 21 ft from the ionization chamber.

5.6 Multiple-plate γ-ray Ionization Chamber. This chamber, similar in principle to that described is Sec. 5.5, was designed for the study of γ-ray pulses produced by a betatron. Its construction is shown in Fig. 5.7.

The γ-ray beam is admitted into the chamber along its axis. A high sensitivity is achieved by the design of the electrode assembly, which consists of 10 thin lead plates alternately connected to a high-voltage supply and to the amplifier input. The brass cylinder that forms the outer case is kept at high voltage while the brass cylinder (3) is grounded. The chamber is filled with a mixture of 95 per cent argon and 5 per cent CO_2; the argon is purified by circulation over hot calcium before being admitted into the chamber. The total gas pressure is approximately 11 atm. The chamber is operated at 2,700 volts.

5.7 Gamma-ray Ionization Chamber with Gas Multiplication. This chamber (see Fig. 5.8) was designed for measuring γ-ray pulses of low intensity. Its construction resembles that of the multiple-wire proportional counter described in Chap. 4, Sec. 4.7. The high-voltage electrode consists of a set of lead plates. The collecting electrode consists of a set of brass diaphragms with circular holes. Across each hole, three thin steel wires are stretched. Gas multiplication takes place at the surfaces of these steel wires. The ionization current corresponding to a given intensity of radiation is enhanced both by the gas multiplication and by the multiple electrode arrangement.

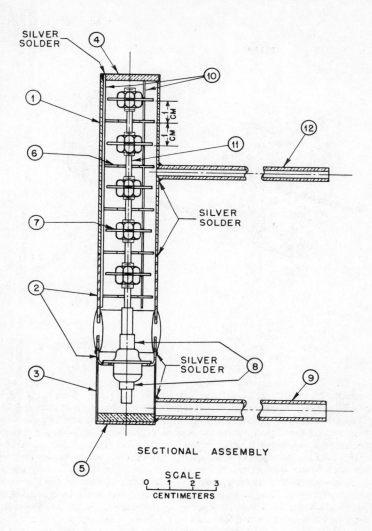

SECTIONAL ASSEMBLY

SCALE
0   1   2   3
CENTIMETERS

Fig. 5.7 — Multiple-plate γ-ray ionization chamber (see Sec. 5.6). 1, brass cylinder, 1 in. OD, 0.025-in. wall. 2, Kovar-glass seal. 3, brass cylinder, 1 in. OD, 0.010-in. wall. 4 and 5, brass end plates. 6, lead disks, 0.040 in. thick, 0.9 in. in diameter, supported at the edges by three brass stems 0.047 in. in diameter and electrically connected to the outer brass case. Two of the stems are shown in the drawing (10). These disks have a central hole 0.350 in. in diameter to permit the passage of the rod (11), which is part of the collecting electrode. 7, lead disks, 0.040 in. thick, 0.8 in. in diameter, supported by the central brass rod (11) and forming the collecting elec- trode. 8, commercial Kovar-glass seal. The Kovar tube at the center of the seal sup- ports the rod (11) bearing the collecting plates. 9, shield for lead to the collecting electrode. 12, gas outlet.

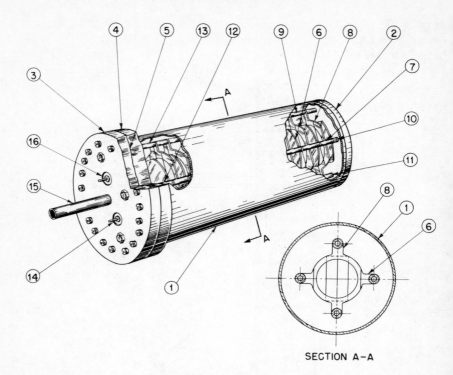

SECTION A–A

Fig. 5.8—Gamma-ray ionization chamber with gas multiplication (see Sec. 5.7). 1, brass tube, 2¾ in. OD, 0.065-in. wall. 2, brass end plate, ¼ in. thick. 3, brass end plate, ¼ in. thick. 4, brass flange. 5, fuse-wire gasket. 6, lead plates, 0.040 in. thick. They are supported by two steel rods with brass spacers, of which one is shown in the diagram (7). These plates form the high-voltage electrode. 8, brass diaphragms with circular holes as shown in detail in the section A-A. Three 0.003-in. steel wires are stretched across the opening ¼ in. apart. The diaphragms are supported by two steel rods with brass spacers (9). These diaphragms form the collecting electrode. 10 and 11, porcelain insulators supporting the high-voltage electrode and the collecting electrode, respectively. They are held in position by metal studs on the end plate (2). 12 and 13, porcelain insulators supporting the high-voltage electrode and the collecting electrode, respectively. They are fastened with screws to the end plate (3). 14 and 16, Kovar-glass seals providing electrcial connection to the high-voltage electrode and to the collecting electrode, respectively. 15, gas inlet.

The chamber is filled at 2 atm with a mixture of 80 per cent argon and 20 per cent methane. Voltages up to 4,000 volts can be used, giving a gas multiplication up to 400. Because of the peculiar transient response of chambers with gas multiplication (Chap. 4, Sec. 4.3), the current will not faithfully follow rapid variations of the γ-ray intensity. Therefore the most useful application of the chamber described above is, in conjunction with an integrating circuit, for the measurement of the integrated intensity of a γ-ray pulse.

5.8 Geiger-Mueller Counters. Figure 5.9 shows the construction of a thin-walled Geiger-Mueller counter designed at the Metallurgical Laboratory for use as a β-ray detector. The cylinder A is machined

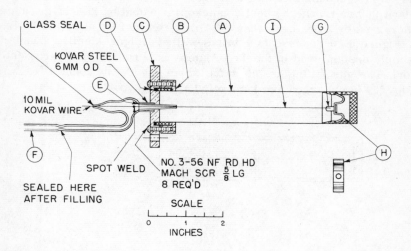

Fig. 5.9— Beta-ray counter (see Sec. 5.8). A, dural cylinder, 0.004 to 0.005 in. wall thickness; this forms the high-voltage electrode. B, brass collar. C, brass end plate. D, neoprene gasket. E, Kovar-glass seal. F, gas inlet. G, pyrex insulator. H, bronze spring clip. I, Kovar wire, 0.005 in. in diameter.

from a solid dural rod to a wall thickness of 0.004 to 0.005 in. The β-ray source is usually in the form of a foil which is wrapped around the cylinder. For many purposes it is important that the wall thickness be uniform so as to ensure uniform absorption of the β-rays. Uniformity of wall thickness will also prevent the cylinder from collapsing when it is evacuated. The counter is assembled in the following way. First the Kovar-glass seal E is soldered into the brass cap C. The central wire assembly, including the pyrex end G, is made and inserted into the bronze spring clip H. This unit is then inserted into the dural tube A so that the ends of the spring fit into the groove cut in A. The dural tube A is then clamped to the cap C by means of the collar B, the Kovar wire protruding through the open end of E. The neoprene gasket D may be made of one piece or from a square strip of neoprene if the ends are carefully fitted together. Finally, the central wire, 0.005 in. thick, is stretched taut, and the Kovar wire at the end is sealed to the glass end of E. The desired tension on the wire may be obtained by clamping the counter in a vertical position and hanging a weight on the end of the wire. The counter is usually filled with a mixture of ethyl alcohol vapor (1 cm Hg pressure) and argon (9 cm Hg pressure). With this mixture, it operates as a self-quenching counter. It ordinarily has a threshold voltage of about 900 volts. In the best counters, the counting rate at the plateau increases by 2 per cent when the voltage is increased by 160 volts.

Figure 5.10 represents a brass-walled Geiger-Mueller counter of simple design, used in the Los Alamos Laboratory as a γ-ray detector. The gas filling is the same as in the β-ray counter shown in Fig. 5.9 (9 cm argon and 1 cm ethyl alcohol vapor).

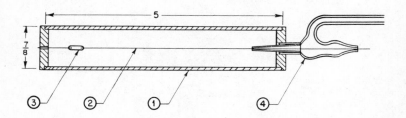

Fig. 5.10—Gamma-ray counter (see Sec. 5.8). 1, brass cylinder, ⅞ in. in diameter, ¹⁄₃₂ -in. wall. 2, 0.005-in. Kovar wire. 3, glass insulator. 4, Kovar-glass seal.

5.9 Mica-window Geiger-Mueller Counter.

Figure 5.11 shows the construction of a mica-window β-ray counter. The counter is prepared and assembled in the following way: The copper cylinder is first washed with 5N nitric acid, rinsed in distilled water, and dried in the oven at 90°C for about 15 min. Then the cylinder is oxidized on the inside by mounting it on top of a test tube containing $Pb(NO_3)_2$. The test tube is heated with a gas burner until the fumes passing through the copper tube have caused its inner surface to acquire an even purple-brown coat.

Then the mica window is mounted thus: The copper flange is heated gently and a ring of high-temperature-melting du Pont Parlou wax is deposited about two-thirds of the way toward the outer edge. The mica is placed on a brass plate, which is uniformly heated electrically. The copper cylinder is set on the mica sheet and the brass plate is kept at a high temperature while the wax flows evenly as far as the outer edge of the flange. The brass ring (8) is also placed on the hot brass plate and covered with wax. The cylinder with the mica window is placed on top of the ring and allowed to cool slowly.

The counters are filled with 90 per cent argon and 10 per cent alcohol to a total pressure of 10 cm Hg. They usually have plateaus of
about 200 volts.

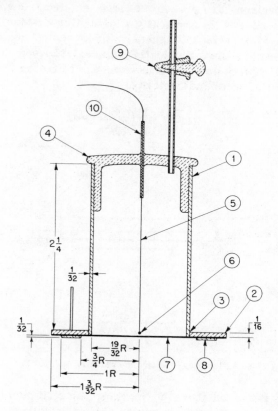

Fig. 5.11—Mica window β-ray counter (see Sec. 5.9). 1, copper cylinder 1¼ in. OD,
⅟₃₂-in. wall. 2, copper flange, ⅟₁₆ in. thick. 3, silver-soldered joint. 4, pyrex-glass
piece, sealed to the copper tube with du Pont high-temperature-melting wax. 5, tungsten wire. 6, pyrex bead, about 0.020 in. in diameter. 7, mica sheet, 3 to 5 mg/sq cm.
8, brass ring. 9, stopcock. 10, metal tube.

5.10 Pulsed Counters. For some special experimental purposes
a simple γ-ray detector was designed, which answers the following
requirements; (1) it has a very small active area; (2) it can be pulsed
(i.e., it can be made sensitive for short predetermined time intervals
of the order of 100 μsec); (3) it provides a sufficiently large output
pulse to operate recorders without need of further amplification, even
through long cables.

The principle adopted in the design of the detector is based upon the fact that, if the voltage across a spark gap is raised somewhat above the so-called "sparking potential," no discharge actually occurs unless electrons are present between the electrodes.

The detector resembles physically a small Geiger-Mueller counter. It is operated with argon filling near atmospheric pressure. A d-c voltage below the sparking potential, applied between cylinder and wire, removes rapidly whatever electrons are liberated in the counter by cosmic rays or local radioactivity.

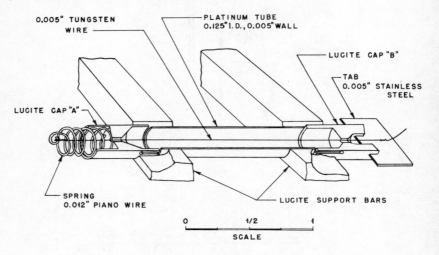

Fig. 5.12 — Pulsed γ-ray counter (see Sec. 5.10).

The voltage is raised above the sparking potential during the appropriate time interval by superimposing a square voltage pulse on the d-c voltage. If, during this time, electrons appear in the counter, they are accelerated toward the wire and initiate a discharge. Positive ions will not give rise to a discharge unless they liberate electrons by striking the cathode, a process that is very unlikely. It follows that a discharge will occur only if an ionizing particle traverses the counter during a time that coincides approximately with the duration of the square voltage pulse. (The sensitive time does not coincide exactly with the duration of the pulse because of the finite transit time of electrons in the counter.)

The design of the counters is affected by the requirement that it should be possible to assemble units containing a large number of closely spaced individual counters. The design adopted is shown in Fig. 5.12. The counter wall is a platinum cylinder of 0.125-in. inside diameter, and 0.005-in. wall thickness. The wire is made of tungsten and is 0.005 in. in diameter. It is supported by lucite caps, which are shaped so as to increase the leakage path along the insulating surface. The individual counter tubes are mounted between two lucite bars, with a spacing of 0.155 in. between the axes of neighboring counters.

The unit was assembled by first sliding the platinum tubes into holes provided in the bars. The wire was then connected to the spring and threaded through the hole of the cap A. The free end of the wire was passed through the platinum cylinder and into the second cap B. After the caps were in position, the wire was stretched and spot-welded to a stainless-steel tab inserted in a slot of the cap B.

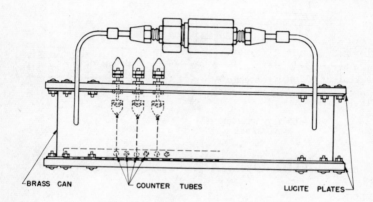

Fig. 5.13—Unit of 50 pulsed γ-ray counters.

The unit was mounted in a gastight box, as shown in Fig. 5.13. Connections to the counter wire leads were brought out through screws inserted in the top lucite plate. The counter cylinders were all connected to a common lead, which was again brought out through the top lucite plate.

A hot-calcium purifier was provided in order to stabilize operation of the counters by removing impurities from the argon filling.

The filling procedure was as follows: The unit was first connected to a vacuum system and evacuated to a pressure of about 10^{-3} cm Hg for several hours. Then the purifier was raised to a temperature of 350°C until the calcium was thoroughly outgassed. Argon was admitted through a dry-ice trap to a pressure of several centimeters of mercury. A glow discharge was passed through each of the counters for several minutes by means of a spark tester. The unit was evacuated again, and finally filled with argon to a pressure of 59 cm Hg.

The electronic equipment used for testing the counters described above is schematically represented by the block diagram in Fig. 5.14.

The pulser produces a square-wave voltage of 450 volts amplitude with a repetition rate of 6 per second. The width of the square wave can be varied from 50 to 200 μsec. This square wave is added by means of an RC coupling network to the base voltage applied to the counter cylinder. The counter wire is connected to ground through a potential divider. When the counter discharges, a pulse of the order of 1,000 volts appears at the wire, and a pulse of the order of 50 volts appears at the point A of the potential divider.

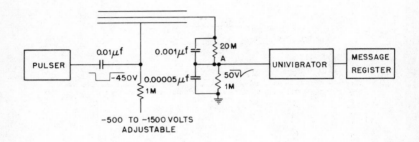

Fig. 5.14 — Schematic diagram of the arrangement used for testing the pulsed counters.

The pulse at point A is sufficient to trigger a univibrator driving a message register. In order to observe the pulse shape, one of the vertical deflecting plates of a cathode-ray tube may be connected to point A. A stationary pattern on the scope is obtained by using a sweep triggered by the pulser.

A number of tests were made on a unit containing 50 individual counters. In these tests, the square wave had a width of 150 μsec.

Figure 5.15 shows the counting rate in an individual counter as a function of the d-c voltage applied to the tube, with a γ-ray source of the order of 1 millicurie placed near the counter. This curve resembles the corresponding curve for an ordinary Geiger-Mueller counter. The counting rate increases from zero to the normal value for an increase of voltage of about 60 volts. The counting rate remains fairly constant over a plateau of 200 to 250 volts width, then starts rising rapidly. "Threshold voltage" may be defined as the voltage at which the counting rate is one-half normal. "Breakdown voltage" may be defined as the voltage at which the counting rate is appreciably above normal.

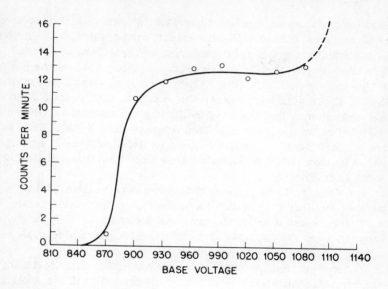

Fig. 5.15—Counting rate as a function of the d-c voltage for a pulsed counter. The square pulses, which determine the sensitive period, had a duration of 150 μsec and an amplitude of 450 volts.

It is obviously desirable that all the counters of a unit have nearly the same characteristics so that they can be operated from the same d-c supply. Figure 5.16 shows threshold voltage and breakdown voltage for the 50 individual counters of the unit used. It appears that the

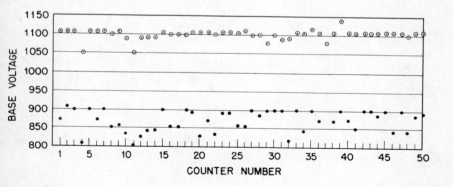

Fig. 5.16—Unit of 50 pulsed counters. Solid dots indicate threshold voltage; dots within circles indicate breakdown voltage.

plateaus of the various counters overlap through a comfortably wide range of voltages. This result was achieved only after thorough cleaning of the counters and careful centering of the wires.

When the γ-ray source is removed, the counting rate on the plateau, for a 150-μsec gate width, drops from a value of about 13 a minute to a value of about 6 an hour. Since the counters are pulsed 6 times a second, this means that the probability for a spontaneous count to be recorded when the counter is pulsed amounts to 1/3,600. This background is sufficiently small for all practical purposes, although it seems to be somewhat higher than that expected from cosmic rays and local radioactivity.

The counting yield of the counter tubes was estimated by determining the counting rate with a known γ-ray source at a known distance. It was found to be of the order of 2 per cent. This is close to the value that can be expected if all of the secondary electrons penetrating the tube give rise to a discharge.

Pulsed counters can be made with metals other than platinum for the counter wall (for instance brass or steel) and with air instead of argon as a gas filling. However, in these counters the background was found to be abnormally large and, moreover, dependent on the history of the counter. High counting rates were recorded immediately after the removal of a strong γ-ray source; this spurious counting rate decreased gradually to the normal background in a period of the order of ½ hr. Furthermore, the operating voltage was a function of the counter history. An explanation for the high counting rate after strong irradiation may be found in the formation of metastable molecules, an effect that is apparently minimized by the use of argon in a platinum counter.

Chapter 6

ALPHA-PARTICLE DETECTORS

6.1 Alpha-particle Spectroscopy. In most cases of interest, the source of α particles is used in solid form. Consequently the material under investigation is deposited as a thin film. If the energy distribution is to be investigated, the detector has to be constructed so that all the particles, regardless of their energy, spend their entire range in the detector. Moreover, the height of the pulses must have a known relation to the particle energy. Suppose a thin film of active material is deposited on one of the electrodes of a plane parallel-plate chamber, such that no α particle escapes from its counting volume. If the chamber is operated as an ion-pulse chamber, the voltage rise of the collecting electrode resulting from every particle will be directly proportional to its energy, regardless of the direction of emission—assuming, of course, constancy of the value of the average energy spent per ion pair. If the chamber is operated as an electron-pulse chamber, the pulse height is proportional to Q_0^-. For α particles originating at the negative electrode Q_0^- is given by the equation

$$Q_0^- = N_0 e (1 - \frac{\bar{x}}{d} \cos \theta) \tag{1}$$

where N_0 is the total number of ion pairs produced by an α particle, $\bar{x}$ is the distance of the center of gravity of ionization from the origin of the track, and θ is the angle between the track and the perpendicular to the electrode (Chap. 3, Sec. 3.5). Since, for an isotropically emitting source, the number of particles emitted between θ and $\theta + d\theta$ is proportional to $\sin \theta \, d\theta$, the number of pulses with height between P and P + dP is given by

$$f(P) \, dP = \text{const. } \sin \theta \, d\theta$$

The quantities θ and P are connected by Eq. 1, considering that P is proportional to Q_0^-. Therefore

$$dP = \text{const. } d(\cos \theta)$$

and

$$f(P) = \text{const.} \qquad (2)$$

The curve representing $f(P)$ is called the differential pulse-height distribution. Equation 2 shows that for the case under consideration $f(P)$ is a constant between P_{max} and P_{min} where

$$\frac{P_{min}}{P_{max}} = \frac{Q_0^- \text{ min}}{Q_0^- \text{ max}} = 1 - \frac{\overline{x}}{d} \qquad (3)$$

The pulses of size P_{min} correspond to particles emitted perpendicularly to the electrode; those of size P_{max} to particles emitted parallel to the electrode. The relative spread of the pulse sizes depends only on the ratio of electrode separation to particle range and the stopping power of the gas used.

In the appendix, Sec. 1, the value of $\overline{x}$ is given as a function of the α-particle energy for various gases. In Fig. 6.1 two experimental distributions measured with α particles from polonium are shown, together with the theoretically expected curves. The finite differential resolution of the detector was taken into account. This is the reason for the finite slope of the theoretical curves at P_{max} and P_{min}.

From the foregoing, it is obvious that the use of plane parallel chambers with electron collection for α-particle spectroscopy would offer great difficulties in the interpretation of the result, since every monochromatic α line would show up as a square distribution of pulses. To avoid this difficulty, a screening grid electrode may be inserted between the collecting and high-voltage electrodes. The grid electrode is placed so far from the negative electrode (carrying the α-particle source) that it is not reached by the α particles. As described in Chap. 3, Sec. 3.2, the grid shields the collecting electrode from the field of the positive ions remaining after the complete collection of the electrons. Consequently, the pulses observed are equal to each other and proportional to N_0. The construction of a grid chamber used for α particles is shown in Chap. 7, Fig. 7.12. The negative electrode, carrying the thin deposit of the α source was kept at −2,500 volts with respect to the collector, and the grid electrode at −1,250 volts. It is rather important for good resolution that the

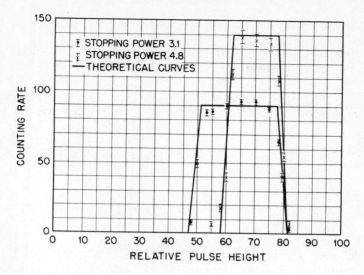

Fig. 6.1 — Differential pulse-height distribution for monoenergetic α particles of polonium in an electron-pulse chamber. Active material on negative electrode. Data taken with stopping powers of 3.1 and 4.8, respectively, to show effect of different values of $\bar{x}/d$. Curves are calculated and corrected for finite channel width of detecting instrument.

grid be at a relatively high negative potential with respect to the collector. The voltage between grid and negative electrode can be small; it should be only high enough to prevent recombination or attachment of the electrons. The high voltage between grid and positive electrode tends to reduce the spread in the sizes of the α-particle pulses since the higher field in the neighborhood of the grid lowers the probability for capture of the electrons by the wires. The grid is constructed to give a maximum of transparency, i.e., to make the fraction of electrons captured by the wires as small as possible. It consists of 3-mil-diameter parallel steel wires, spaced $\frac{1}{16}$ in. apart.

With a chamber filling of 7.5 atm argon and a normal sample of uranium i.e., U^{234} in equilibrium with U^{238}, the differential pulse-height distribution given in Fig. 6.2 was obtained. It shows the two groups of α particles well resolved and of about the same intensity. As indicated in the figure, the width of the peaks is only slightly larger than the channel width of the detector.

Spectral distributions could also be determined quite conveniently by accurate range measurements. However, it was found that the results obtained by the pulse-height method described above showed considerably better resolution, since the straggling in range has no effect on the pulse size.

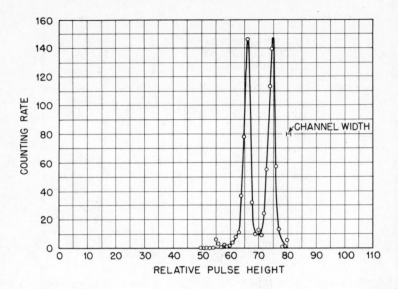

Fig. 6.2 — Differential pulse-height distribution for α particles of normal uranium (U [234] and U [238] in equilibrium) in an electron-pulse chamber with grid.

6.2 <u>Absolute Counters</u>. Very often the α activity of a sample must be measured to determine the half-lives or the amount of α-active material. For this purpose the size of a pulse produced by the particle is of minor importance. It is necessary, however, to determine accurately the number of α particles emitted within an accurately known solid angle per unit time.

If the material is present in the form of a thin deposit (thin compared to the range of the α particles in the material) backed by a heavy plate, the arrangement is called a "2π detector." Usually it is built in the form of a simple plane parallel-plate chamber with such dimensions that any α particle traversing the counting volume produces a pulse large enough to be counted. Ideally the solid angle subtended for every nucleus of the sample is 2π. Thus, the detection efficiency defined as the number of counts divided by the number of disintegrations should be

$$F = \frac{1}{2}$$

However, two corrections must be applied. The first arises from the finite thickness t of the active material. Particles emerging under an almost grazing angle with respect to the foil surface may have undergone such a high energy loss on their long path in the material that they cannot produce a pulse of sufficient height to be counted. This results in a reduction of the efficiency, which now depends on the bias energy B. The quantity B is defined as the minimum pulse height that is detected. As shown in the appendix, Sec. 6, F(B) is given by the equation

$$F(B) = \frac{1}{2} \left\{ 1 - \frac{t}{2[R_0 - R(B)]} \right\} \tag{4}$$

where R_0 is the range of the α particles in the material of the source and R(B) is the range of an α particle of energy B. F(B) represents also the so-called "integral pulse-height distribution":

$$F(B) = \int_B^\infty f(P)\, dP \tag{5}$$

where f(P) is normalized so that $\int_0^\infty f(P)\, dP$ is equal to the ratio of the number of particles penetrating the chamber to the total number of disintegrations.

The second correction is due to back-scattering of the α particles caused by the plate supporting the active material and by the material itself. The back-scattering of an α particle traveling in the material in a direction away from the counting volume will give rise to an increased counting rate. The number of α particles moving toward the counting volume and being scattered toward the backplate is obviously smaller than the number of those scattered into the counter by the backplate, since the former ones traverse only a small amount of material. From Rutherford's formula it follows that the back-scattering, due to a single scattering process, is extremely small due to the small probability for scattering under a large angle. However, a noticeable increase of particles in the counter volume is caused by a large number of multiple scattering processes under small angles. The problem was treated theoretically at the Metallurgical Laboratory. It is assumed that if an initially narrow and parallel beam of α particles has traveled through a sufficient layer of material, the density of particles in a radial direction in the plane perpendicular to the beam will show a Gaussian distribution. Under this assumption the detection efficiency is given by the equation

$$F(B) = \frac{1}{2} \left\{ 1 - \frac{t}{2[R_0 - R(B)]} + 0.201\, \Phi(B) \right\} \tag{6}$$

where the second term is the thickness correction as before, and the term $0.201\,\Phi\,(B)$ is the back-scattering correction. The quantity Φ is a function of the initial range R_0 of the α particle and of the residual range $R(B)$, and it depends on the material in which back-scattering takes place. Numerical values of Φ are given in the appendix, Sec. 12. For a thin layer of α-active material, backed by a solid thick plate, the back-scattering does not depend on the thickness t of the active layer.

An example of a 2π counter is shown in Fig. 6.3. The active material is spread over a circle of 3.1 cm diameter on a platinum foil

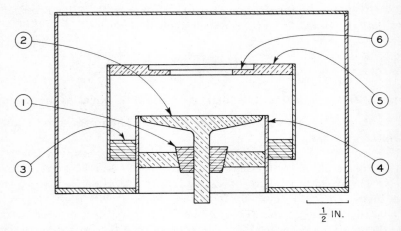

$\frac{1}{2}$ IN.

Fig. 6.3 — Parallel-plate-type 2π counter for absolute measurement of the number of α particles emitted by a source. 1, polystyrene insulator. 2, collecting electrode. 3, amphenol insulator. 4, guard electrode. 5, high-voltage electrode. 6, holder for plate carrying the source.

which is mounted on the negative electrode of the chamber. The separation of the electrodes is 1.2 cm. The chamber is filled with 1.5 atm of argon. The back-scattering for a uranium source was determined experimentally and theoretically with the results.

$$0.201\ \Phi = 0.013 \quad \text{(experimentally)}$$

$$0.201\ \Phi = 0.016 \quad \text{(theoretically)}$$

An arrangement known as a "4π counter," which permits quantitative counting of α particles and avoids the effect of back-scattering is shown in Fig. 6.4. It consists of a brass block in which two over-lapping cylindrical openings have been drilled. Two thin wires are mounted along the axes of the two cylinders, thus forming two pro-portional counters. The wires are supported on one side by metal-glass seals, on the other by lucite disks. The α-active material is deposited on a very thin collodion foil that is mounted over the window of the foil holder (see detail). The foil holder is inserted into a slot between the two counters. In this way all the α particles emitted over the full solid angle 4π are detected. The counting rate is not affected by back-scattering and only the thickness correction has to be applied. It was found to be unnecessary to ensure conductivity on both sides of the collodion. The counters are filled with 1 atm of argon and oper-ated with a voltage of -810 volts at the wall. A bias curve is shown in Fig. 6.5.

6.3 <u>Range Measurements</u>. A very simple arrangement for the measurement of the range of α particles is shown in Fig. 6.6. The ionization chamber, of the parallel-plate type, and the foils carrying a thin layer of the α-active material are both supported by a track. This makes it possible to reproduce exactly the relative distance between chamber and source. The whole arrangement is placed in an airtight container filled with argon at approximately 1 atm pressure. An accurate manometer is used to measure the pressure. In order to determine the range, the number of counts is measured as a function of the pressure in the container with the sample at a fixed distance from the chamber. If absolute range measurements are desired, this distance should be rather large in order to avoid excessive variations in the path length of the various particles. The chamber is very shal-low (0.1 cm). The front electrode is formed by a grid of parallel wires 0.014 in. in diameter and spaced $\frac{1}{32}$ in. apart. The chamber is operated at 400 volts. The bias of the detecting equipment has to be set so low that any α particle traversing the chamber at the lowest pressure in the container is counted.

A typical number-vs.-pressure curve obtained with this apparatus is shown in Fig. 6.7. The simplest procedure to obtain accurate values of the range consists in comparing the unknown sample with a standard, such as polonium. If the unknown sample and the standard are both thin (layer thickness very small compared to the range) and are spread over the same area, the mean range R_x in standard air of the unknown sample is

$$R_x = R_0 + d \cdot \left(\frac{\Delta p}{760}\right)_{15°} \cdot s \qquad (7)$$

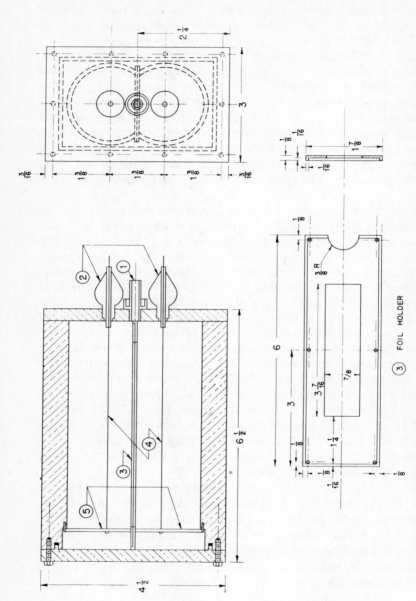

Fig. 6.4 — 4π proportional counter for absolute measurement of the number of α particles emitted by a source. 1, gas inlet. 2, Kovar-glass seals. 3, holder for foil. 4, collecting electrodes (0.004-in. platinum wire). 5, lucite disks supporting the collecting electrodes.

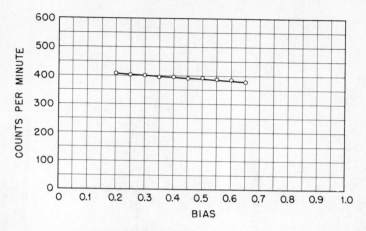

Fig. 6.5 — Bias curve of 4π counter (shown in Fig. 6.4); thin collodion foil with thin uranium coating. The ordinate represents the sum of the counting rates of both counters.

where R_0 is the mean range in standard air (see appendix, Sec. 1) of the standard, d is the distance of the samples from the chamber, s is the stopping power of the gas relative to air* for an energy of the α particle corresponding to a range $(R_x + R_0)/2$, and Δp is the pressure difference for corresponding points of number-vs.-pressure curves for the unknown and the standard source. As corresponding points of the two curves, one might, for instance, take those at which the counting rates are one-half of the maximum. The value of d is obtained from the measurement with the standard. If the α particles were collimated, the pressure $p_{\frac{1}{2}}$ at which half-maximum counting rate occurs would be related to the mean range R_0 and the distance d by

$$d = \left(\frac{760}{p_{\frac{1}{2}}}\right)_{15°} \cdot \frac{R_0}{s} \tag{8}$$

where s is the stopping power relative to air for α particles of mean range R_0. This procedure is not quite correct, since the lack of collimation makes the abscissa at half-maximum counting rate slightly smaller than the mean range. The error, however, enters only in the

*s is defined as the ratio of the stopping numbers for the gas under consideration and for air (see appendix, Sec. 1).

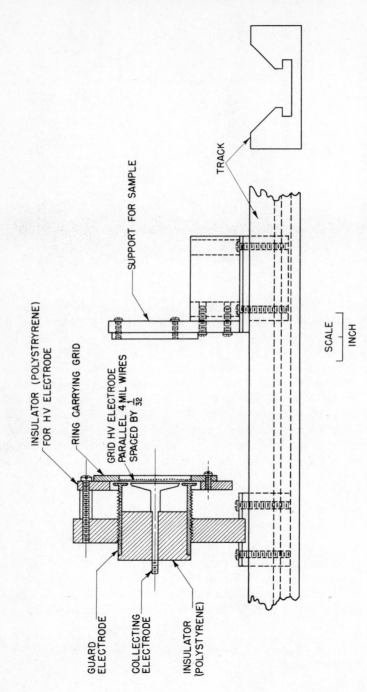

Fig. 6.6—Arrangement of source and ionization chamber for range measurements.

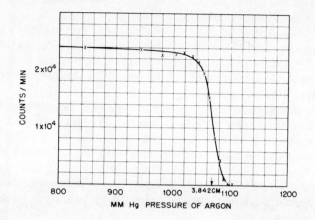

Fig. 6.7—Counting rate vs. pressure taken with apparatus of Fig. 6.6 with a polonium sample. Distance from source to chamber, 2.84 cm.

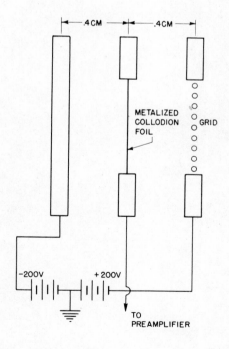

Fig. 6.8—Differential chamber for range measurements of α particles (schematic).

computation of the difference in range between standard and unknown samples and is therefore small.

The data shown in Fig. 6.7 were obtained with a thin sample of polonium spread over a circle of 1 cm diameter at a distance of 2.84 cm. It may be pointed out that argon is particularly suitable as a gas filling, since its stopping power relative to air is very nearly independent of the α-particle energy.

For range measurements of samples with several ranges, differential ionization chambers have been used. The arrangement is schematically shown in Fig. 6.8. The ions produced by α particles that cross both sections of the chamber induce on the collecting electrode opposite and nearly equal charges. Therefore they give rise to small pulses, which can be biased off, and only particles ending in the front half of the double chamber are recorded. With polonium samples differential α-particle distributions with a width at half-maximum of 0.3 cm air at N.T.P. were obtained. This width is considerably more than the one observed with grid chambers using the pulse-height method, where (see Fig. 6.2) the width at half-maximum corresponds to about 0.13 cm.

Chapter 7

DETECTORS FOR NEUTRON RECOILS

7.1 <u>Introductory Considerations</u>. The chambers described in the present section were designed to detect recoils produced when neutrons collide elastically with atomic nuclei.

In the laboratory system, let E_n be the energy of the neutron before the collision and θ the angle between the lines of flight of the incoming neutron and of the recoil nucleus. From the principles of conservation of energy and momentum, the energy E of the recoil is

$$E = \frac{4A}{(1 + A)^2} \, E_n \, \cos^2 \theta \qquad (1)$$

where A is the mass number of the nucleus. The recoil energy E is a maximum for a head-on collision ($\theta = 0$), in which case it has the value

$$E_{max} = \frac{4A}{(1 + A)^2} \, E_n \qquad (2)$$

Another useful relation is that connecting the recoil energy E with the angle of scattering φ of the neutron in the frame of reference where the center of gravity of the neutron and the nucleus is at rest. This relation is

$$E = \frac{2A}{(1 + A)^2} \, E_n \, (1 - \cos \varphi) \qquad (3)$$

Let σ_s be the integral scattering cross section and $\sigma(\varphi)$ be the differential scattering cross section in the center-of-gravity system. Then $[\sigma(\varphi) \, d\omega]/\sigma_s$ represents the probability that in a collision the neutron will be scattered through the angle φ, into the element of solid angle $d\omega$, where φ and $d\omega$ are measured in the center-of-gravity system. The probability $p(E)\, dE$ for the nucleus to acquire in a collision a recoil energy between E and E + dE is then given by

$$p(E)\, dE = \frac{\sigma(\varphi)}{\sigma_s}\, 2\pi \sin \varphi \, d\varphi$$

where φ is the function of E defined by Eq. 3. It follows

$$p(E) = \frac{\sigma(\varphi)}{\sigma_s}\, \frac{\pi}{E_n}\, \frac{(A+1)^2}{A} \qquad (4)$$

Equation 4 expresses a simple relation between the energy distribution of the recoil nuclei in the laboratory system and the angular distribution of the scattered neutrons in the center-of-gravity system.

The maximum recoil energy decreases as the mass number increases. Hence the recoils of highest energy always arise from the elements of lowest mass number present in the gas or in the walls of the chambers. In order to interpret the observations quantitatively, one element present in the active volume of the chamber should be considerably lighter than all the others, and the experiment should be arranged in such a way as to detect only recoils of higher energy arising from this lighter element.

Recoil chambers may be classified according to the nature of the light element from which the recoils are produced and according to whether this element is part of the gas or is contained in a film on the walls of the chamber. In the latter case a further distinction may be made between thin radiators, i.e., radiators of a thickness smaller than the range of the fastest recoils, and thick radiators, i.e., those of a thickness larger than the range of the fastest recoils. Recoil chambers also differ according to their geometry (parallel-plate, cylindrical, spherical, etc.) and according to the method of detection of the ionization (electron-pulse chamber, ion-pulse chamber, proportional counter, integrating chamber).

7.2 General Properties of Hydrogen Recoil Chambers. Hydrogen is an outstanding radiator for recoil chambers for several reasons. At most energies its scattering cross section is appreciably larger than that of other light nuclei. The cross section is well-known, at least in the energy region, from about 0.4 to 5.0 mev (see the appendix, Sec. 4). The cross section is a smooth function of the energy (no resonances), and the energy of hydrogen recoils is larger than that of recoils from any other element.

For hydrogen, Eqs. 1 and 2 become

$$E = E_n \cos^2 \theta \tag{5}$$

$$E_{max} = E_n \tag{6}$$

For energies below 10 mev, the scattering of neutrons on protons is spherically symmetric in the center-of-gravity system, i.e.,

$$\frac{\sigma(\varphi)}{\sigma_s} = \frac{1}{4\pi}$$

It follows then from Eq. 4 that the probability p(E) dE of a hydrogen recoil of energy (E, dE) being produced in a collision is given by

$$p(E) = \frac{1}{E_n} = \text{const.} \qquad \text{for } E < E_n$$
$$p(E) = 0 \qquad\qquad\quad \text{for } E > E_n \tag{7}$$

The energy loss per centimeter divided by the energy per ion pair (see the appendix, Sec. 2) gives the specific ionization, i.e., the number of ion pairs per centimeter. A fairly good approximation for the energy-range relation in the high-energy region is

$$R = \alpha E^{\frac{3}{2}} \tag{8}$$

where α is a constant. From this equation one obtains for the energy loss

$$-\frac{dE}{dx} = \frac{1}{(dR/dE)} = \frac{2}{3\alpha} E^{-\frac{1}{2}} \tag{9}$$

Both expressions (Eqs. 8 and 9) are grossly inaccurate for low energies (less than 0.4 mev). In this region, a better approximation is given by

$$R = \alpha E^{\frac{3}{2}} + \beta E \tag{8a}$$

$$-\frac{dE}{dx} = \frac{1}{\frac{3}{2}\alpha E^{\frac{1}{2}} + \beta} \tag{9a}$$

where α and β are two constants.

Section 7.3 and following sections describe the distribution in size of ionization pulses for monoenergetic neutrons produced in hydrogen recoil chambers of different design. The functions representing the differential pulse-height distributions will be normalized to give the number of pulses per unit pulse-height interval divided by the total number of recoil protons produced in the radiator. Correspondingly, the functions representing the integral pulse-height distributions will be normalized to give the number of pulses larger than a certain amount, relative to the total number of recoils. With this normalization, the value of the integral pulse-height-distribution function corresponding to a given value P of the pulse height coincides with the detection efficiency for a bias energy B = P. The detection efficiency is here defined as the ratio of the number of counts to the number of secondary processes produced in the radiator.

It is convenient to measure pulse heights in terms of the neutron energy E_n, rather than in electron volts (see Chap. 3, Sec. 3.3). In other words, it is convenient to express the differential and integral pulse-height distributions by means of functions of the ratio P/E_n [$f(P/E_n)$ and $F(P/E_n)$, respectively]. If P is a function of the recoil energy alone, $f(P/E_n)$ is related to the probability $p(E)$ defined previously by the equation

$$f\left(\frac{P}{E_n}\right) = E_n p(E) \frac{dE}{dP} \tag{10}$$

The efficiency ϵ of a radiator, defined as the average number of hydrogen recoils produced when a neutron traverses the chamber, has, for monoenergetic neutrons, the expression

$$\epsilon(E_n) = t\nu\, \sigma_s(E_n) \tag{11}$$

where t is the thickness, in micrograms per square centimeter, of the radiator for the neutron beam under consideration; ν is the number of hydrogen atoms per microgram in the radiator; and $\sigma_s(E_n)$ is the neutron-scattering cross section for hydrogen. Table 7.1 gives

Table 7.1 — Efficiency ϵ of a Glycerol Tristearate Radiator of 100 μg/sq cm as a Function of Neutron Energy E_n

E_n, mev	0.1	0.5	2	6
$\epsilon \times 10^5$	9.56	4.84	2.23	0.97

the efficiency as a function of energy for a film of glycerol tristearate $(C_{57}H_{110}O_6)$ of 100 μg/sq cm.

In the case of monoenergetic neutrons, the counting yield η (i.e., the number of counts per neutron traversing the chamber) is given by the equation

$$\eta = \epsilon(E_n) \; F\left(\frac{B}{E_n}\right) = t\nu \, \sigma_s(E_n) \; F\left(\frac{B}{E_n}\right) \tag{12}$$

where B is the bias energy.

7.3 Infinitely Thin Solid Radiator: Ion-pulse Chamber, Electron-pulse Chamber with Grid, or Proportional Counter; No Wall Correction. In this case no appreciable amount of energy is dissipated by the recoil protons in the radiator, and the chamber is supposed to be sufficiently deep so that none of the protons hit the walls. Hence, the energy dissipated by each proton in the chamber is equal to its original recoil energy. Moreover, on account of the method of detection, the pulse height P is equal to the energy dissipated. Therefore

$$P = E = E_n \; \cos^2 \theta \tag{13}$$

Now assuming that the chamber is irradiated with neutrons of the same energy E_n, the differential pulse-height distribution, according to Eqs. 7 and 10, is given by

$$\begin{aligned} f\left(\frac{P}{E_n}\right) &= 1 \qquad \text{for } \frac{P}{E_n} < 1 \\[2mm] f\left(\frac{P}{E_n}\right) &= 0 \qquad \text{for } \frac{P}{E_n} > 1 \end{aligned} \tag{14}$$

The corresponding integral pulse-height distribution is

$$F\left(\frac{P}{E_n}\right) = \int_{P/E_n}^{1} f\left(\frac{P'}{E_n}\right) \; d\left(\frac{P'}{E_n}\right) = 1 - \frac{P}{E_n} \tag{15}$$

The counting yield of the chamber for a bias energy B (see Eq. 12) can be written as

$$\eta = t\nu \, \sigma_s(E_n) \; \left(1 - \frac{B}{E_n}\right) \tag{16}$$

In first approximation, the scattering cross section of hydrogen, in the energy region between 0.05 and 3 mev, may be assumed to be inversely proportional to the square root of the energy, so that

$$\sigma_s(E_n) = \sigma_0 E_n^{-\frac{1}{2}} \tag{17}$$

where σ_0 = constant. With this expression for σ_s, Eq. 16 becomes

$$\eta = \epsilon_B \left(\frac{E_n}{B}\right)^{-\frac{1}{2}} \left(1 - \frac{B}{E_n}\right) \tag{16a}$$

where

$$\epsilon_B = t\nu\sigma_0 B^{-\frac{1}{2}}$$

represents the efficiency of the radiator for neutrons of energy $E_n = B$ (see Eq. 11). Notice that the counting yield is a function of the ratio of the neutron energy to the bias energy. The behavior of this function is shown in Fig. 7.1. The yield η is obviously zero for E < B. It

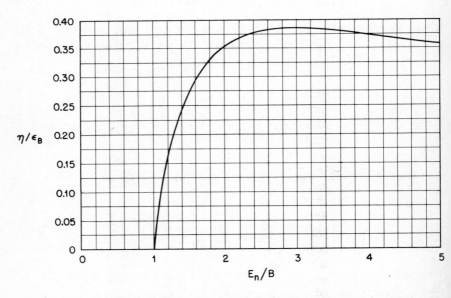

Fig. 7.1 — Ion-pulse parallel-plate chamber with infinitely thin radiator or ion-pulse gas-recoil chamber with negligible wall effects. Counting yield η is in terms of the efficiency ϵ_B at the bias energy, as a function of the ratio E_n/B of the neutron energy to the bias energy.

reaches a maximum for $E_n = 3B$, which may be found by differentiation of Eq. 16. From this maximum the yield decreases very slowly.

7.4 Infinitely Thin Solid Radiator: Parallel-plate Electron-pulse Chamber; No Wall Correction. As in Sec. 7.3, the energy loss of the recoil protons in the radiator is negligible, and the protons are supposed to dissipate all their energy in the sensitive volume of the chamber. However, the pulse height is no longer equal to the energy dissipated in the chamber but is the energy multiplied by the distance of the "center of gravity" of the ionization from the positive electrode divided by the distance between the electrodes. Assume that the radiator is placed on the negative electrode and that the neutrons are incident perpendicularly upon it, as shown in Fig. 7.2. Let d be the distance between the electrodes and p the pressure of the gas in atmospheres.

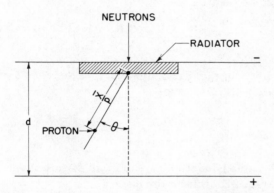

Fig. 7.2 — Parallel-plate recoil chamber with solid radiator.

Now consider a recoil of energy E emitted from the radiator under an angle θ, and let $\bar{x}/p$ be the distance from the origin of the recoil track to the center of gravity of the ionization. The pulse height produced by the recoil under consideration is then given by

$$P = \left(1 - \frac{\bar{x} \cos \theta}{pd}\right) E \qquad (18)$$

Since the specific ionization is proportional to the energy loss, $\bar{x}$ has the general expression

$$\bar{x} = \frac{1}{E} \int_0^R \left(-\frac{dE}{dx}\right) x \, dx \qquad (19)$$

where energy losses and ranges are relative to the gas under consideration at 1 atm pressure. The value of $\bar{x}$ for various gases, as a function of energy, is given in the appendix, Sec. 1. For sufficiently large recoil energies, the expressions given by Eqs. 8 and 9 can be used for R and $-dE/dx$ to obtain

$$\bar{x} = \tfrac{3}{5}R = \tfrac{3}{5}\alpha E^{\frac{3}{2}} \tag{20}$$

Considering Eq. 5, Eq. 18 becomes

$$P = \left(1 - \frac{3}{5}\frac{R}{pd}\sqrt{\frac{E}{E_n}}\right)E \tag{21}$$

which can also be written as

$$\frac{P}{E_n} = \frac{E}{E_n} - \frac{3}{5}\frac{R_0}{pd}\left(\frac{E}{E_n}\right)^3 \tag{21a}$$

where $R_0 = \alpha E_n^{\frac{3}{2}}$ is the maximum range of the recoil protons. Differentiating Eq. 21a gives

$$\frac{dP}{dE} = \frac{d(P/E_n)}{d(E/E_n)} = 1 - \frac{9}{5}\frac{R_0}{pd}\left(\frac{E}{E_n}\right)^2 \tag{21b}$$

E is a single-valued function of P only if dP/dE never changes sign. According to Eq. 21b, this is the case if

$$R_0 \leq \tfrac{5}{9}\,pd \tag{22}$$

If, however, $R_0 > \tfrac{5}{9}\,pd$, there are recoils of two different energies, emerging from the radiator at two correspondingly different angles and giving rise to pulses of the same size.

When the inequality in expression 22 is satisfied, the maximum pulse size corresponds to the maximum recoil energy, i.e.,

$$\frac{P_{max}}{E_n} = 1 - \frac{3}{5}\frac{R_0}{pd} \tag{23}$$

When condition 22 is not satisfied, the maximum pulse size is that for which dP/dE vanishes, i.e.,

$$\frac{P_{max}}{E_n} = \frac{2}{9}\left(\frac{5pd}{R_0}\right)^{\frac{1}{2}} \tag{23a}$$

If condition 22 is satisfied, the differential pulse-height distribution $f(P/E_n)$ can be written, according to Eqs. 7, 10, and 21b, as

$$f\left(\frac{P}{E_n}\right) = \frac{1}{1 - \dfrac{9}{5}\dfrac{R_0}{pd}\left(\dfrac{E}{E_n}\right)^2} \qquad \text{for } P < P_{max}$$

$$= 0 \qquad \text{for } P > P_{max}$$

(24)

where E is given as a function of P by Eq. 21a.

Graphs of $f(P/E_n)$ for various values of the parameter R_0/pd are given in Fig. 7.3. The area under all curves is 1, since all the recoil

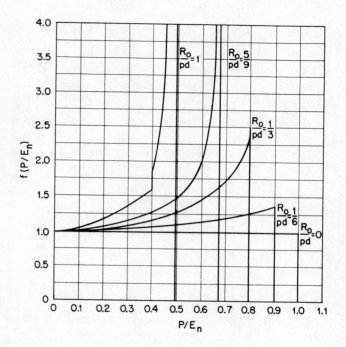

Fig. 7.3—Electron-pulse parallel-plate chamber with infinitely thin hydrogenous radiator on one plate. Differential pulse-height distribution of hydrogen recoils produced by monoenergetic neutrons falling perpendicularly upon the radiator, for different values of the ratio between the maximum range R_0/p of the recoils in the gas and the depth d of the chamber.

protons produced in the radiator penetrate the active volume of the chamber. For $R_0/pd = 0$, the function $f(P/E_n)$ reduces to a constant as in the case discussed in the preceding section. For $R_0/pd = \frac{5}{9}$,

$f(P/E_n)$ becomes infinity at $P = P_{max}$. For $R_0/pd > ⅝$, the function exhibits peculiarities on account of the multiple-valued relation between E and P. The function $f(P/E_n)$ for the case under consideration has also been calculated by using the energy-range relation given in the appendix, Sec. 1, instead of the $E^{\frac{3}{2}}$ law. The results are summarized in Table 7.2.

Table 7.2 — Differential and Integral Pulse-height Distributions for Argon-filled Parallel-plate Electron-pulse chambers with Glycerol Tristearate Radiators

$E_n = 0.3$ mev; pd = 4.02 atm × cm

P/E_n	t = 0	t = 25 μg/sq cm		t = 50 μg/sq cm		t = 75 μg/sq cm	
	f	f	F	f	F	f	F
0.1666	1.0083	0.8430	0.7410	0.7449	0.6622	0.6864	0.6045
0.3333	1.0122	0.8935	0.5960	0.8159	0.5337	0.7642	0.4853
0.5000	1.0476	0.9557	0.4420	0.8931	0.3945	0.8485	0.3531
0.6000	1.0695	1.0004	0.3425	0.9444	0.3007	0.9020	0.2644
0.6666	1.0874	1.0260	0.2735	0.9773	0.2355	0.9396	0.2024
0.7000	1.0979	1.0393	0.2385	0.9952	0.2022	0.9613	0.1701
0.7333	1.1088	1.0562	0.2050	1.0166	0.1697	0.9854	0.1383
0.7666	1.1203	1.0742	0.1700	1.0375	0.1362	1.0082	0.1055
0.7848	1.1278	1.0850	0.1500	1.0496	0.1168	1.0216	0.0864
0.8386	1.1508	1.1145	0.0915	1.0830	0.0605	0.7220	0.0400
0.8909	1.1773	1.1467	0.0300	0.5733	0.0150	0.3822	0.0100
0.9423	1.2040	0.0000	0.0000	0.0000	0.0000	0.0000	0.0000

$E_n = 0.4$ mev; pd = 4.02 atm × cm

P/E_n	t = 0	t = 25 μg/sq cm		t = 50 μg/sq cm		t = 75 μg/sq cm	
	f	f	F	f	F	f	F
0.1250	1.0073	0.8151	0.8005	0.7117	0.7358	0.6568	0.6890
0.2500	1.0201	0.8835	0.6910	0.7990	0.6393	0.7449	0.5990
0.3750	1.0414	0.9471	0.5760	0.8818	0.5348	0.8343	0.5006
0.5000	1.0735	1.0084	0.4545	0.9582	0.4218	0.9188	0.3933
0.6250	1.1262	1.0776	0.3220	1.0385	0.2967	1.0063	0.2731
0.7500	1.2015	1.1664	0.1820	1.1358	0.1618	1.1099	0.1425
0.7750	1.2219	1.1898	0.1530	1.1606	0.1330	1.1360	0.1140
0.8000	1.2434	1.2133	0.1235	1.1866	0.1037	1.1640	0.0845
0.8204	1.2622	1.2341	0.0985	1.2095	0.0790	1.1885	0.0594
0.8518	1.2926	1.2676	0.0605	1.2458	0.0407	0.8306	0.0271
0.8829	1.3292	1.3064	0.0190	0.6532	0.0095	0.4355	0.0063
0.9117	1.3624	0.0000	0.0000	0.0000	0.0000	0.0000	0.0000

Table 7.2 (Continued)

$E_n = 0.5$ mev; pd $= 4.02$ atm $\times$ cm

P/E_n	t = 0	t = 25 μg/sq cm	t = 50 μg/sq cm	t = 75 μg/sq cm
	f	f	f	f
0.4000	1.0649	0.9963	0.9424	0.9004
0.5000	1.1088	1.0591	1.0173	0.9822
0.6000	1.1733	1.1364	1.1033	1.0748
0.7000	1.2702	1.2438	1.2188	1.1959
0.7600	1.3533	1.3308	1.3071	1.2854
0.8000	1.4250	1.4016	1.3827	1.3653
0.8208	1.4691	1.4479	1.4295	1.4132
0.8396	1.5146	1.4947	1.4771	0.9847
0.8581	1.5652	1.5454	0.7727	0.5151
0.8756	1.6090	0.0000	0.0000	0.0000

$E_n = 0.6$ mev; pd $= 4.02$ atm $\times$ cm

P/E_n	t = 25 μg/sq cm	t = 50 μg/sq cm	t = 75 μg/sq m		t = 100 μg/sq cm	t = 175 μg/sq cm	
	f	f	F	f	F	F	f	F
0.1666	0.8507	0.7576	0.7488	0.7103	0.7181			
0.2500	0.9228	0.8491	0.6798	0.7995	0.6538	0.6303	0.6826	0.5710
0.3333	0.9825	0.9246	0.6067	0.8818	0.5843	0.5634	0.7740	0.5101
0.4166	1.0447	1.0001	0.5258	0.9634	0.5076	0.4904	0.8651	0.4429
0.5000	1.1141	1.0805	0.4408	1.0502	0.4246	0.4095	0.9660	0.3665
0.5833	1.2004	1.1756	0.3482	1.1534	0.3336	0.3194	1.0823	0.2812
0.6666	1.3329	1.3151	0.2440	1.2968	0.2313	0.2192	1.2351	0.1852
0.7000	1.4087	1.3772	0.1998	1.3569	0.1876	0.1762	1.3082	0.1434
0.7333	1.5083	1.4889	0.1507	1.4692	0.1401	0.1295	1.4144	0.0982
0.7524	1.5686	1.5485	0.1223	1.5329	0.1111	0.1008	1.4782	0.0720
0.7649	1.6113	1.5934	0.1027	1.5794	0.0962	0.0822		0.0530
0.7770	1.6631	1.6491	0.0837	1.6357	0.0736	0.0631		0.0377
0.7892	1.7306	1.7169	0.0623	1.7030	0.0520	0.0414		0.0237
0.8010	1.7951	1.7806	0.0425	1.7654	0.0321	0.0241		0.0138
0.8126	1.8619	1.8471	0.0220		0.0147	0.0110		0.0063
0.8243	1.9375		0.0050		0.0033	0.0025		0.0014
0.8351	0.0000	0.0000	0.0000	0.0000	0.0000	0.0000		0.0000

Table 7.2 (Continued)

$E_n = 0.6$ mev; $pd = 8.98$ atm × cm				$E_n = 1.0$ mev; $pd = 8.98$ atm × cm			
	t = 0	t = 175 μg/sq cm			t = 0	t = 175 μg/sq cm	
P/E_n	f	f	F	P/E_n	f	f	F
0.1666	1.0077		0.6231	0.10			0.7527
0.2500	1.0149	0.6668	0.5732	0.15			0.7217
0.3333	1.0255	0.7416	0.5141	0.20	1.0188	0.70387	0.6884
0.4167	1.0405	0.8098	0.4501	0.25	1.0311	0.76750	0.6524
0.5000	1.0591	0.8746	0.3790	0.30	1.0456	0.82845	0.6120
0.5873	1.0821	0.9347	0.3038	0.35	1.0652	0.88625	0.5692
0.6666	1.1125	0.9927	0.2231	0.40	1.0872	0.93923	0.5244
0.7500	1.1594	1.0555	0.1377	0.45	1.1179	0.99250	0.4750
0.8000	1.1935	1.0966	0.0832	0.50	1.1526	1.0479	0.4241
0.8160	1.2049	1.1112	0.0681	0.55	1.1979	1.1089	0.3705
0.8480	1.2257	0.8293	0.0359	0.60	1.2597	1.1819	0.3123
0.8796	1.2530	0.5209	0.0121	0.65	1.3319	1.2652	0.2545
0.9260	1.2937	0.0000	0.0000	0.70	1.4412	1.3802	0.1870
				0.75	1.5988	1.5432	0.1131
				0.78	1.7188	1.6859	0.0645
				0.8017	1.8499	1.8004	0.0322
				0.8109	1.9046	1.3360	0.0161
				0.8201	2.0576	0.8350	0.0058
				0.8336	2.0685	0.0000	0.0000

$E_n = 1.6$ mev; $pd = 8.98$ atm × cm		$E_n = 1.6$ mev; $pd = 12.70$ atm × cm		
	t = 175 μg/sq cm		t = 175 μg/sq cm	
P/E_n	F	P/E_n	f	F
0.1250	0.7928	0.1250		0.7942
0.1562	0.7713	0.1875		0.7512
0.1875	0.7467	0.2500	0.8634	0.6949
0.2187	0.7217	0.3125	0.9415	0.6391
0.2500	0.6948	0.3750	1.0204	0.5775
0.2812	0.6658	0.4375	1.1064	0.5110
0.3125	0.6360	0.5000	1.2101	0.4393
0.3437	0.6068	0.5625	1.3554	0.3604
0.3750	0.5705	0.5937	1.4539	0.3155
0.4062	0.5359	0.6250	1.5978	0.2685
0.4375	0.4988	0.6562	1.7768	0.2180
0.4687	0.4588	0.6875	2.1253	0.1575
0.5000	0.4185	0.7187	2.6720	0.0840
0.5312	0.3719	0.7250	2.8800	0.0670
0.5625	0.3180	0.7312	3.1360	0.0485
0.5937	0.2565	0.7375	3.4720	0.0280

Table 7.2 (Continued)

| $E_n = 1.6$ mev; pd = 8.98 atm × cm | | $E_n = 1.6$ mev; pd = 12.70 atm × cm | | |
| t = 175 μg/sq cm | | t = 175 μg/sq cm | | |
P/E_n	F	P/E_n	f	F
0.6250	0.1730	0.7404	3.8803	0.0190
0.6375	0.1180	0.7416	3.9782	0.0137
0.6469	0.0000	0.7429	2.9136	0.0093
		0.7441	2.3936	0.0061
		0.7454	1.8432	0.0032
		0.7468	1.2621	0.0014
		0.7477	0.6485	0.0004
		0.7489	0.0000	0.0000

7.5 <u>Thin Solid Radiator: Parallel-plate Ion-pulse Chamber, Electron-pulse Chamber with Grid, or Proportional Counter; No Wall
Correction.</u> This case is similar to that discussed Sec. 7.3 except
that the thickness of the radiator, even though smaller than the maximum range of the recoil protons in the radiator itself, is not negligible compared with this range. Assume that the radiator is placed on
one of the plates of the chamber and that monoenergetic neutrons of
energy E_n fall perpendicularly upon it, as indicated in Fig. 7.2. The
recoil protons that give a pulse larger than P are those that emerge
from the radiator with an energy larger than P. If $R'(E)$ represents
the range in the material of the radiator of protons of energy E, a
proton, generated in the radiator at a depth x, at an angle θ, will produce a pulse larger than P if x ≤ X, where X satisfies the equation

$$R'(E) - \frac{X}{\cos \theta} = R'(P)$$

or

$$R'(E) - X \sqrt{\frac{E_n}{E}} = R'(P) \tag{25}$$

Hence, the total number of pulses larger than P, relative to the
total number of recoils generated in the radiator, is given by

$$F = \frac{1}{tE_n} \int_P^{E_n} X(E) \, dE \tag{26}$$

where X is either the thickness t of the radiator or the function of E defined by Eq. 25, whichever is smaller. Assuming $R'(E)$ proportional to $E^{\frac{3}{2}}$, Eq. 25 becomes

$$X = R_0' \ \sqrt{\frac{E}{E_n}} \ \left[\left(\frac{E}{E_n} \right)^{\frac{3}{2}} - \left(\frac{P}{E_n} \right)^{\frac{3}{2}} \right] \tag{25a}$$

where R_0' is the range in the radiator of protons of energy E_n. Equation 26 can then be written as follows

$$F\left(\frac{P}{E_n} \right) = \int_{P/E_n}^{1} \frac{1}{t} X \left(\frac{E}{E_n}, \frac{P}{P_n} \right) \ d\left(\frac{E}{E_n} \right) \tag{26a}$$

Since X/t is either 1 or a function of R_0'/t, E/E_n, and P/E_n, Eq. 26a shows that, under the assumption made, the function F depends only on the ratios P/E_n and R_0'/t. The same is true for the differential pulse-height distribution, which is obtained by differentiating F with respect to P/E_n.

The functions $f(P/E_n)$ and $F(P/E_n)$ have been calculated, assuming R' proportional to $E^{\frac{3}{2}}$, and the results are given in Fig. 7.4.

The areas under the curves for $f(P/E_n)$ corresponding to different thicknesses of the radiator are not equal. The reason is that, as the radiator becomes thicker, an increasing fraction of the recoils produced in the radiator are absorbed by the radiator itself before they reach the active volume of the chamber.

7.6   Thin Solid Radiator: Parallel-plate Electron-pulse Chamber; No Wall Correction. This case is similar to that discussed in Sec. 7.4, except for the finite thickness of the radiator. The differential and integral pulse-height distributions for this case were calculated, on the basis of the energy-range relations given in the appendix, Sec. 1, for radiators of glycerol tristearate $(C_{57}H_{110}O_6)$ in argon-filled chambers.

These results are summarized in Table 7.2, where f and F are given as a function of P/E_n for various values of the neutron energy E_n, the radiator thickness t, and the product pd of the gas pressure times the depth of the chamber.

In Fig. 7.5 the functions $f(P/E_n)$, corresponding to $t = 0$ and $t = 175$ μg/sq cm and calculated for the same value of E_n (1 mev) and pd (8.98 atm × cm), are represented graphically in order to illustrate the influence of a finite radiator thickness on the pulse-height-distribution curves. The differential pulse-height distribution for $t = 0$, calculated on the basis of the $R \propto E^{\frac{3}{2}}$ approximation, is also represented in the same figure. The difference between this curve and that

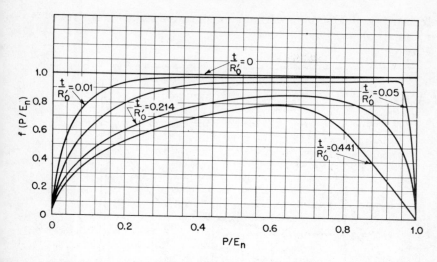

Fig. 7.4a — Ion-pulse parallel-plate chamber with thin hydrogenous radiator on one plate. Differential pulse-height distribution of hydrogen recoils produced by monoenergetic neutrons falling perpendicularly upon the radiator for different values of the ratio t/R_0' between the thickness of the radiator and the maximum range of the recoils in the radiator.

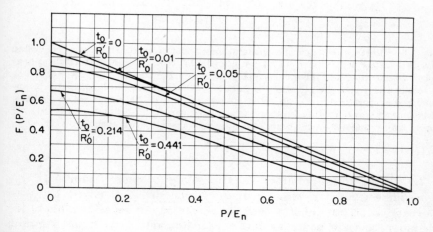

Fig. 7.4b — Ion-pulse parallel-plate chamber with thin hydrogenous radiator on one plate. Integral pulse-height distribution of hydrogen recoils produced by monoenergetic neutrons falling perpendicularly upon the radiator for different values of the ratio t/R_0' between the thickness of the radiator and the maximum range of the recoils in the radiator.

calculated on the basis of the more accurate energy-range relation is very small.

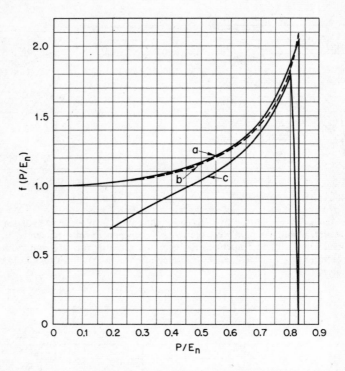

Fig. 7.5—Electron-pulse parallel-plate chamber with glycerol tristearate radiator on one plate. Plate separation d = 1.34 cm; gas fills 6.7 atm of argon. Differential pulse-height distribution for hydrogen recoils produced by neutrons of 1 mev energy falling perpendicularly upon the radiator. (a) Infinitely thin radiator (t = 0), calculated by assuming R proportional to $E^{\frac{3}{2}}$. (b) Infinitely thin radiator (t = 0), calculated on the basis of the energy-range relation given in the appendix, Sec. 1. (c) "Thin" radiator (t = 175 μg/sq cm), calculated on the basis of the energy-range relation given in the appendix, Sec. 1.

7.7 Thick Solid Radiator: Parallel-plate Ion-pulse Chamber, Electron-pulse Chamber with Grid, or Proportional Counter; No Wall Correction. The radiator is again placed on the negative plate of the chamber, and the neutrons fall perpendicularly upon it, as shown in Fig. 7.2. The thickness of the radiator is now supposed to be larger than the range R_0' of the fastest recoil protons in the radiator.

The integral pulse-height distribution in the case of monoenergetic neutrons striking the chamber is given by Eq. 26 or 26a where

$X(E_n, P, E)$ is now defined in every case by Eq. 25, i.e., it never becomes equal to the thickness t of the radiator. If the range is assumed to be proportional to $E^{\frac{3}{2}}$, then Eq. 25a holds and

$$F\left(\frac{P}{E_n}\right) = \int_{P/E_n}^1 \frac{R_0'}{t}\left[\left(\frac{E}{E_n}\right)^{\frac{3}{2}} - \left(\frac{P}{E_n}\right)^{\frac{3}{2}}\right]\sqrt{\frac{E}{E_n}}\ d\left(\frac{E}{E_n}\right)$$

or

$$F\left(\frac{P}{E_n}\right) = \frac{R_0'}{3t}\left[1 - \left(\frac{P}{E_n}\right)^{\frac{3}{2}}\right]^2 \tag{27}$$

The counting yield of the chamber for a bias energy B (see Eq. 12) is expressed as

$$\eta = \tfrac{1}{3}\nu\sigma_s(E_n)\ R_0'\ \left[1 - \left(\frac{B}{E_n}\right)^{\frac{3}{2}}\right]^2 \tag{28}$$

or, if R' is assumed to be proportional to $E^{\frac{3}{2}}$ and σ_s proportional to $E_n^{-\frac{1}{2}}$

$$\eta = \tfrac{1}{3}\zeta_B \frac{E_n}{B}\ \left[1 - \left(\frac{B}{E_n}\right)^{\frac{3}{2}}\right]^2 \tag{28a}$$

In the above equation

$$\zeta_B = R'(B)\nu\sigma_0 B^{-\frac{1}{2}}$$

represents the average number of recoils per incident neutron of energy $E_n = B$ produced in a thickness of the radiator equal to the range of protons of energy B. Equation 28a indicates that η is a function of E_n/B. A graph of this function is given in Fig. 7.6. Notice there that the counting yield of a recoil chamber with thick radiator increases rapidly and continuously with increasing neutron energy.

7.8 Gas Recoil Chamber; No Wall Effects. Assume now that the chamber is filled with pure hydrogen, a hydrogen compound, or a hydrogen-containing mixture, and that the linear dimensions of the chamber are very large compared with the range of the fastest recoil protons, so that wall effects can be disregarded.

If the chamber is used as an ion-pulse chamber, P = E and the differential and integral pulse-height distribution for monoenergetic neutrons are the same as in Sec. 7.3 (Eqs. 14 and 15). If the chamber is used as an electron-pulse chamber, the pulse-height distribution depends on the geometry.

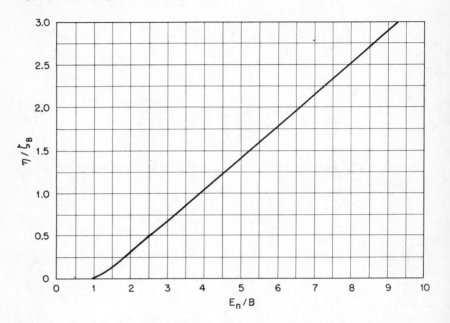

Fig. 7.6 —Ion-pulse parallel-plate chamber with thick radiator. Counting yield η is in terms of $\zeta_B = \nu \sigma_0 B^{-\frac{1}{2}} R'$ (B) as a function of the ratio E_n/B of the neutron energy to the bias energy.

If the chamber is used as an integrating chamber and is filled with pure hydrogen, the intensity I of the ionization current is given by

$$I = H \frac{E_n}{2} \frac{e}{W_0} \qquad (29)$$

where H is the number of recoils per second produced in the chamber, e is the electron charge, W_0 is the energy per ion pair, and $E_n/2$ is the average energy of the hydrogen recoils.

7.9 Gas-recoil Ion-pulse Chamber; Computation of Wall Effects. Let us consider two types of ionization chambers: a parallel-plate chamber with a circular collecting electrode, surrounded by a guard ring as shown in Fig. 7.7; a cylindrical chamber with axial collecting electrode supported by guard electrodes as shown in Fig. 7.8.

In both cases the sensitive volume is supposed to be sharply defined and in the shape of a cylinder with flat ends. The direction of the incoming neutrons is parallel to the axis of the cylinder, as shown by the arrows. In the case of Fig. 7.7 the wall effects are caused: (1) by

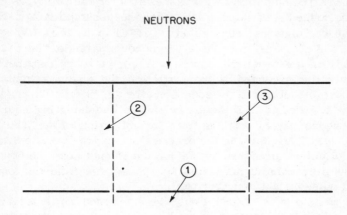

Fig. 7.7—Wall effects in a gas-recoil parallel-plate chamber with circular electrodes.

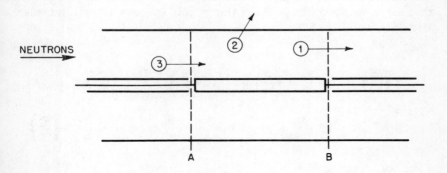

Fig. 7.8—Wall effects in a gas-recoil cylindrical chamber.

recoils hitting the electrode at the far end of the chamber; (2) by recoils produced in the sensitive volume but going out of the sensitive volume through its lateral boundary; (3) by recoils produced outside the sensitive volume and entering the sensitive volume through its lateral boundary. In the case of Fig. 7.8, the wall effects are caused: (1) by recoils produced in the sensitive volume and crossing the boundary B; (2) by recoils hitting the lateral wall; (3) by recoils produced outside the sensitive volume and entering the sensitive volume through the boundary A. The recoils hitting the central electrode are neglected.

A general computation fo the wall effects for the two types of chambers described was carried out under the assumption that $R = \alpha E^{\frac{3}{2}}$. In these calculations, edge effects (see Chap. 3, Sec. 3.7) were neglected, and therefore the pulse height for a particle that crossed the boundary of the sensitive volume was computed by considering only the ionization produced by the particle in the sensitive volume. This procedure is justified if the conditions for an "ideal" ion-pulse chamber are fulfilled, i.e., if the decay time of the detecting equipment is very long compared with the time for collection of the positive ions (see Chap. 3, Sec. 3.6). In the practical cases, the peculiarities in the shape of pulses produced by the motion of ions near the boundary of the sensitive volume may have an appreciable influence on the observed pulse-height distribution.

The results of the calculations are expressed by the equations below, in which b represents the radius of the cylindrical sensitive volume and a its length (a is the spacing of the plates in the case of Fig. 7.7 or the length of the collecting electrode in the case of Fig. 7.8). These results apply to chambers of any dimensions, provided that the maximum range R_0 of the recoil protons is smaller than a. Case (a) (see Fig. 7.7):

$$f\left(\frac{P}{E_n}\right) = 1 + \frac{R_0}{a} A\left(\frac{P}{E_n}\right) + \frac{R_0^2}{ab} B\left(\frac{P}{E_n}\right) + \frac{R_0}{b} C\left(\frac{P}{E_n}\right)$$

$$F\left(\frac{P}{E_n}\right) = \left(1 - \frac{P}{E_n}\right) + \frac{R_0}{a} D\left(\frac{P}{E_n}\right) + \frac{R_0^2}{ab} G\left(\frac{P}{E_n}\right) + \frac{R_0}{b} H\left(\frac{P}{E_n}\right) \qquad (30)$$

Case (b) (see Fig. 7.8):

$$f\left(\frac{P}{E_n}\right) = 1 + \frac{R_0}{a} L\left(\frac{P}{E_n}\right) + \frac{R_0^2}{ab} M\left(\frac{P}{E_n}\right) + \frac{R_0}{b} N\left(\frac{P}{E_n}\right)$$

$$F\left(\frac{P}{E_n}\right) = \left(1 - \frac{P}{E_n}\right) + \frac{R_0}{a} Q\left(\frac{P}{E_n}\right) + \frac{R_0^2}{ab} S\left(\frac{P}{E_n}\right) + \frac{R_0}{b} T\left(\frac{P}{E_n}\right) \qquad (31)$$

The functions A, B, C, D, G, H, L, M, N, Q, S, and T are given in Table 7.3.

Table 7.3 — Functions Entering in Eqs. 30 and 31

P/E_n	A	B	C	D	G	H	L	M	N	Q	S	T
0	0.750	0.0879	0.187	0	-0.0273	0.125	0.750	0.0439	0.1875	0.3333	-0.01367	0
0.1	0.659	0	0.296	-0.0707	-0.0311	0.0964	0.965	0	0.1419	0.242	-0.0149	-0.01653
0.2	0.542	-0.0485	0.295	-0.131	-0.0286	0.0647	0.949	-0.0434	0.0944	0.1454	-0.01209	-0.0284
0.3	0.4025	-0.0785	0.252	-0.178	-0.0224	0.0373	0.861	-0.0607	0.0481	0.0544	-0.00688	-0.0355
0.4	0.243	-0.0826	0.190	-0.211	-0.0139	0.0152	0.344	-0.0640	0.00506	-0.0248	-0.000590	-0.0381
0.6	-0.1286	-0.0637	0.0608	-0.223	0.00277	-0.0101	0.286	-0.0318	-0.0637	-0.1278	0.00985	-0.0318
0.8	-0.554	0.0155	-0.0436	-0.156	0.00801	-0.0110	-0.300	0.0345	-0.0945	0.1287	0.00975	-0.0152
1.0	-1.000	0	0	0	0	0	-1.000	0	0	0	0	0

7.10   Uses of Recoil Chambers.   Recoil chambers are used for the following purposes:

1. Relative flux measurements of neutron beams with the same energy distribution.

2. Absolute flux measurements for monoenergetic neutron beams.

3. Determination of the energy distribution of neutrons.

4. Investigation of neutron scattering on light atomic nuclei.

For (1), (2), and (3) hydrogen recoil chambers are generally used. No special precautions are needed in the construction of a chamber for relative measurements of neutron flux. High sensitivity, small physical size, and directionality may be desirable features. Examples of chambers designed to satisfy one or the other of these requirements will be found below.

The problem of building a chamber for absolute flux measurements is a much more difficult one. In the first place it is necessary to know the efficiency ϵ of the radiator. In the case of a gas recoil chamber, this implies an accurate knowledge of the sensitive volume, of the total gas pressure, and of the concentration of hydrogen in the gas of the chamber. In the case of a solid radiator, the mass of the foil and its chemical composition must be accurately known. The radiator is generally prepared by distillation in a vacuum, and if it is made of a material (such as ordinary paraffin) containing different chemical species, the composition of the foil may be different from that of the bulk material. Mainly for this reason, the radiators for quantitative flux measurements were prepared with glycerol tristearate, which is a definite chemical compound, rather than with paraffin.

In the second place, it is necessary to determine the fractional number of recoils produced in the chamber that are detected with the specific experimental arrangement. If no collimation of the recoil protons is used (see below), the pulses obtained range in size all the way from 0 to a maximum. Only the pulses above a certain size, B, are detected, where B is determined by the bias setting. It is necessary first to know B in absolute value, i.e., in terms of energy, and then to evaluate the quantity $F(B/E_n)$, which represents the fractional number of recoils giving pulses larger than B. This requires a simple geometrical design of the chamber, so that $F(B/E_n)$ may be calculated theoretically. It requires also an experimental check of the calculated pulse-height distribution. The experimental check is necessary for three reasons:

1. It provides the only reliable method for the calibration of the bias setting in terms of energy, i.e., for the absolute determination of B.

2. It determines the lowest bias at which only hydrogen recoils are detected. In addition to hydrogen recoils, the chamber usually has recoils of other light nuclei (argon, carbon, etc.), as well as secondary electrons produced by γ rays. If the resolving time of the detecting equipment is not small compared with the average time separation of the spurious pulses, these latter will "pile up" and give rise to pulses larger than those that an individual recoil or secondary electron could produce (see the appendix, Sec. 11). The bias at which spurious pulses of the type described start being counted is generally characterized by a sudden departure of the experimental from the theoretical pulse-height-distribution curve.

3. Finally, in many cases the experimental pulse-height-distribution curves do not agree with the calculated ones, even for bias energies at which it would seem unlikely to detect pulses due to spurious recoils or to secondary electrons from γ rays. There may be many reasons for discrepancies between experiment and theory, such as: lack of monochromaticity of the neutrons, either inherent in the neutron source or produced by inelastic scattering of the neutrons in the material of the chamber; incorrect evaluation of the edge effects (see Chap. 3, Sec. 3.7); range straggling or error in the evaluation of the energy-range relation (only likely in the low-energy region); lack of proportionality between the number of ions and pulse height; and spread in pulse height when chambers with gas multiplication are used (see Chap. 4, Sec. 4.6). Often the actual source of the trouble cannot be determined, but it is clear that no chamber should be used for absolute neutron-flux measurements unless the theoretical and experimental pulse-height-distribution curves agree.

It maybe pointed out that measurement of the differential pulse-height distribution provides a much more rigorous check on the behavior of the chamber than the determination of the integral pulse-height distribution. It may also be noted that accurate results can be obtained only if the bias can be set sufficiently low to count a large fraction of the recoils produced in the radiator.

Another possible method for determining the ratio of the number of recoils detected to the total number of recoils produced is to collimate the recoil protons in such a way that only those enter the chamber that are ejected within a certain angle θ_0, with the direction of the incoming neutrons. These protons have energies above $E_n \cos^2 \theta_0$, and if this value is sufficiently large the bias can be adjusted so that all the protons are detected. In this way, the fractional number of recoils detected is determined by the geometrical arrangement rather than by the bias setting. An example of a detector based on this principle is described in Sec. 7.19.

Finally, absolute measurements of neutron flux may be made with a gas-recoil integrating ionization chamber (see Sec. 7.8). An instrument of this type is described in Sec. 7.18.

Chambers used as neutron spectrometers must satisfy requirements somewhat different from those laid down for the chambers used for absolute flux measurements. Only the energy dependence of the efficiency, not its absolute value, need be known. However, the pulse-height distribution for monoenergetic neutrons must be accurately known, and it must be of a sufficiently simple shape that the neutron spectrum may be calculated from the observed distribution of recoil pulses.

In principle, an ideal neutron spectrometer would have a very thin radiator and have both the incident neutrons and the recoil protons well collimated. Such a chamber would give pulses of a single size for each neutron energy. The drawback to this arrangement is the low sensitivity resulting from double collimation. For this reason no detectors of the type described were built at the Los Alamos Laboratories. They may, however, be useful for some specific applications.

The second choice for a neutron spectrometer is a chamber in which a monoenergetic neutron beam gives a constant differential pulse-height distribution (infinitely thin radiator, ion-pulse chamber; gas-recoil ion-pulse chamber of very large dimensions; etc.). In this case, if $N(E_n)\,dE_n$ represents the number of incident neutrons with energy between E_n and $E_n + dE_n$, and if $\psi(P)\,dP$ represents the number of pulses observed with the height between P and $P + dP$, the following equation holds (see Eq. 14):

$$\psi(P)\,dP = \text{const. } dP \int_{E_n = P}^{\infty} \frac{1}{E_n}\,N(E_n)\,\sigma_S(E_n)\,dE_n$$

From this it follows that

$$N(E_n) = \text{const. } \frac{E_n}{\sigma_S(E_n)}\left(-\frac{d\psi}{dP}\right)_{P = E_n} \tag{32}$$

Chambers approximating this type were built and used successfully (see Secs. 7.11 and 7.12).

For the investigation of scattering cross sections, the chambers used must be of sufficiently simple design that the energy distribution of the recoils may be deduced from the observed pulse-height distribution. Equation 4 shows that the energy distribution of recoils in the laboratory system gives the differential scattering cross section in the center-of-gravity system.

7.11 **High-pressure Gas-recoil Ion-pulse Chamber.** Figure 7.9 shows the construction of a chamber used as a neutron spectrometer. This chamber is similar in design to one described by Barschall and Kanner.* The sensitive volume is a cylinder 8.5 cm in diameter and 8.5 cm high. To obtain a sufficiently high field through the large sensitive volume, the latter is divided into six sections by grids of ⅛-in. mesh made of annealed copper wire of 0.008-in. diameter. The transparency of each grid is thus about 87 per cent. The solid plates, which limit the sensitive volume at the top and at the bottom, as well as grids 2 and 4, are connected to form the high-voltage electrode. Grids 1, 3, and 5 are similarly connected to form the collecting electrode. Each of the three grids that form the collecting electrode is mounted on a thin brass ring. This is supported on two small amber beads on a wider brass ring, which forms the guard electrode. Each of the three collecting grids also carries a tongue that protrudes through a slot of the guard electrode into a grounded brass tube containing the connecting lead (see detail). The capacity of the collecting-electrode assembly is approximately 60 $\mu\mu$f.

The chamber was used with pressures up to 26 atm of pure hydrogen or hydrogen-argon mixtures. Before entering the chamber the gas was freed from organic vapors and water. A small amount of oxygen (0.01 per cent) was added to produce negative ions and thus prevent the occurrence of the fast part of the pulse, which is due to the motion of free electrons. The chamber was usually operated at 6,000 volts. The pulse amplifier had a rise time of 0.5 milliseconds and a decay time of 2.0 milliseconds. This small bandwidth was used in order to minimize the noises. The chamber, despite its sturdy construction, is very sensitive to microphonic disturbances. It is also very sensitive to γ rays because of the high pressure used. The large value of the decay-time constant of the amplifier, which is required in order to avoid excessive distortion of the ion pulses, enhances the probability of large spurious pulses produced by the piling up of γ-ray pulses. In the absence of γ rays, it was found possible to record recoil protons down to an energy of about 0.6 mev.

The advantages of the chamber are the high counting yield (of the order of 1 or 2 per cent) and the lack of directionality (except for the wall-effect corrections).

*Barschall and Kanner, Phys. Rev., 58, (1940).

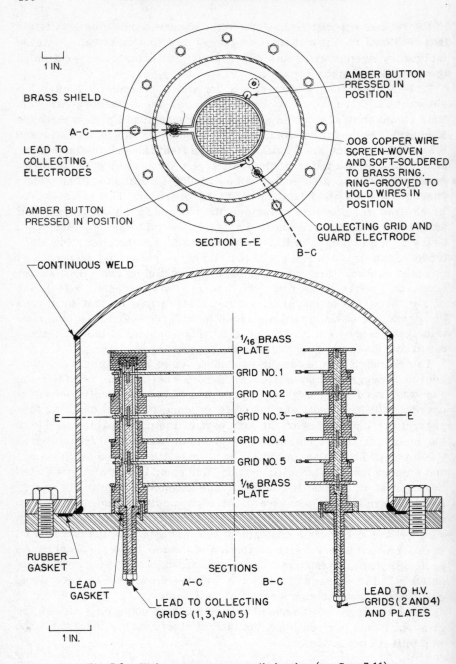

1 IN.

BRASS SHIELD

A-C

LEAD TO
COLLECTING
ELECTRODES

AMBER BUTTON
PRESSED IN POSITION

AMBER BUTTON
PRESSED IN
POSITION

.008 COPPER WIRE
SCREEN-WOVEN
AND SOFT-SOLDERED
TO BRASS RING.
RING-GROOVED TO
HOLD WIRES IN
POSITION

COLLECTING GRID AND
GUARD ELECTRODE

B-C

SECTION E-E

CONTINUOUS WELD

1/16 BRASS
PLATE

GRID NO. 1

GRID NO. 2

GRID NO. 3

GRID NO. 4

GRID NO. 5

1/16 BRASS
PLATE

E   E

RUBBER
GASKET

LEAD
GASKET

LEAD TO COLLECTING
GRIDS (1, 3, AND 5)

SECTIONS

A-C   B-C

LEAD TO H.V.
GRIDS (2 AND 4)
AND PLATES

1 IN.

Fig. 7.9 — High-pressure gas-recoil chamber (see Sec. 7.11).

The wall-effect corrections can be expressed by the following equation, which gives the differential pulse-height distribution:

$$f\left(\frac{P}{E_n}, E_n\right) = \alpha(E_n)\left[1 + \mu(E_n)\,E_n\left(1 - \frac{P}{E_n}\right)\right] \qquad (33)$$

The quantities α and μ depend on the neutron energy E_n and on the gas pressure. For a sufficiently high pressure, or for a sufficiently low energy, $\alpha = 1$, $\mu = 0$, and Eq. 33 becomes Eq. 14, which represents the pulse-height distribution when wall effects can be neglected (see Secs. 7.8 and 7.3). For a gas filling, with a stopping power equivalent to that of 39 atm of H_2, α is represented by the curve in Fig. 7.10, while $\mu(E_n)$ is given approximately by

$$\mu(E_n) = 0.23\,(E_n - 0.6) \qquad \text{for } E_n > 0.6$$
$$\mu(E_n) = 0 \qquad\qquad\quad \text{for } E_n < 0.6$$

where E_n is measured in million electron volts. The neutrons are assumed to travel in a direction perpendicular to the electrodes of the chamber.

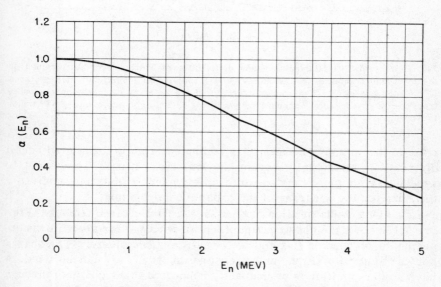

Fig. 7.10—Values of the function $\alpha(E_n)$, which enters Eq. 33.

The performance of the chamber was tested by irradiating it with monoenergetic neutrons of 2.5 mev energy obtained from the D-D reaction. Observed pulse-height distribution is represented by curve a, Fig. 7.11. Curve b in the same figure represents the energy spec-

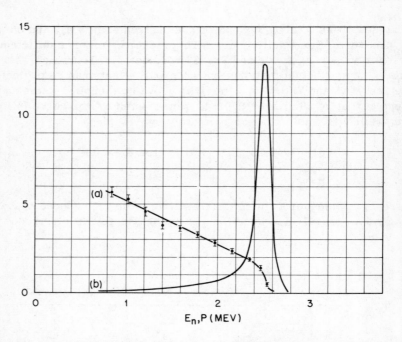

Fig. 7.11 — (a) Differential pulse-height distribution of hydrogen recoils obtained by means of the chamber described in Sec. 7.11 irradiated with monoenergetic neutrons of 2.5 mev energy. (b) The energy spectrum of the primary neutrons, as computed from the observed recoil distribution; gas filling 13.8 atm of argon plus 2.73 atm of hydrogen.

trum of the primary neutrons, as computed from the observed recoil distribution, taking into account the wall corrections. The extent to which curve b approximates an infinitely narrow distribution gives a measure for the accuracy of the experimental method.

7.12 Thin-radiator Electron-pulse Parallel-plate Chamber. Figure 7.12 shows the construction of a chamber used for absolute measurements of neutron flux and as a neutron spectrometer. The chamber is filled with argon, and pressures up to 7 atm can be used. A hot-calcium purifier is permanently connected to the chamber through two $\frac{3}{8}$-in. steel pipes (not shown in the diagram). This makes it possible to purify the gas whenever necessary. The chamber is normally operated at −2,000 volts.

The radiator is a glycerol tristearate film of about 180 $\mu g/\text{sq cm}$ prepared by evaporation in a vacuum. It is placed on a platinum foil, which is part of the high-voltage electrode. Extensive tests were made in order to make sure that the conductivity of the foil was sufficiently large to prevent accumulation of charges which might disturb the electric field and therefore distort the pulse-height distribution. For these tests, a polonium source was deposited on a platinum foil and then covered with a glycerol tristearate film. The platinum foil thus prepared was placed in the chamber in place of the radiator and the pulse-height distribution of the α particles determined. Then a 1-g radium source was placed near the chamber to produce an intense ionization of the gas. The radium source was removed and the pulse-height distribution remeasured immediately afterwards. The pulse-height distributions measured before and after irradiation proved to be identical. This result was taken as a proof that, even in the presence of an ionization much heavier than that existing under normal operating conditions, the glycerol tristearate film does not acquire a charge sufficient to distort the pulse-height distribution.

The collecting electrode and the attached lead have a capacity of 10 to 15 $\mu\mu\text{f}$. The chamber was used with an amplifier having a rise time of 2 μsec and a decay time constant of 20 μsec. The small value of the latter time constant practically eliminates microphonic disturbances and makes it possible to operate the chamber in the presence of fairly strong γ radiation. The minimum pulse height that can be measured safely is approximately 0.2 mev. The maximum neutron energy for which the chamber can be used is determined by the condition that the maximum range of the recoil protons should be not more than five-ninths the spacing of the electrodes (Sec. 7.4). This energy is about 2 mev.

In the construction of the chamber care was taken to avoid heavy materials in the path of the incident neutrons so as to minimize the danger of inelastic scattering. All metal parts in contact with the sensitive volume of the chamber were gold-plated and then outgassed by heating in vacuum in an effort to minimize the background caused by recoils from hydrogen absorbed in the metal. This background was experimentally determined by irradiating the chamber with neutrons after replacing the radiator with a blank platinum foil. The number of recoils recorded under these conditions was about 10 per cent of the number recorded with the radiator in place.

The chamber can be used with or without the grid (1) shown in Fig. 7.12a. When used, the grid is kept at a voltage of $-1,400$ volts with respect to the collecting electrode (the high-voltage electrode is kept at $-2,000$ volts). The operation of the chamber was tested with and without the grid by determining the pulse-height distribution with a

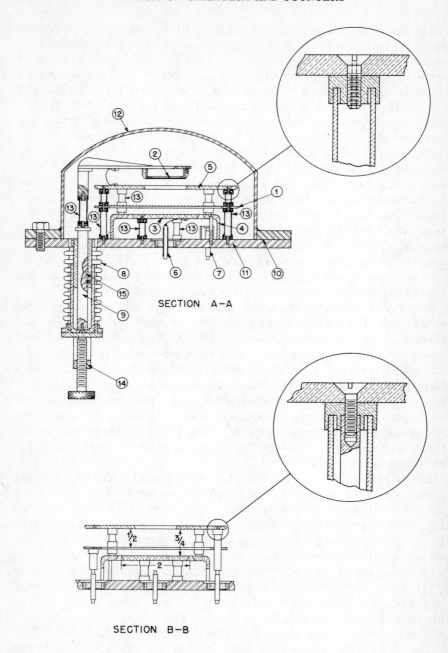

SECTION A–A

SECTION B–B

Fig. 7.12a — See facing page for legend.

polonium source on a platinum foil in place of the radiator. Without the grid, the pulse-height distribution should be "rectangular" if the measurements are taken with a channel discriminator of infinitesimal width, or "trapezoidal" if a channel discriminator of finite width is used (see Chap. 6, Sec. 6.1).

With the grid, all the α-particle pulses should be of the same size (see Chap. 3, Sec. 3.2 and Chap. 6, Sec. 6.1). The experimental curves confirm these predictions (see Chap. 6, Figs. 6.1 and 6.2).

The chamber was also tested — again with and without the grid — by determining the pulse-height distribution of the hydrogen recoils when the chamber was placed in a monoenergetic neutron beam falling normally upon the radiator. The curves obtained were of the expected shape. As an example, Fig. 7.13 gives the results of measurements taken with the grid in position. In this case, if an infinitely narrow channel is used and if the radiator is infinitely thin, the pulse-height distribution should be "constant," as described in Sec. 7.3.

7.13 Thin-radiator Electron-pulse Parallel-plate Double Chamber. This chamber, based on the same principle as that described in Sec. 7.12, was designed primarily to measure fission cross sections. It consists essentially of a single case containing a fission chamber and a recoil chamber, the latter being used as a neutron-flux meter. The fissionable material and a thin layer of hydrogenous material are deposited on two thin platinum foils, which are placed back to back to form the common high-voltage electrode of the two chambers. Thus the two samples are almost exactly in the same plane and are separated by an amount of material that does not produce any appreciable amount of scattering or absorption of the neutron beam. The neutron flux is therefore the same for both samples and the ratio of the cross sections is simply equal to the ratio of the number of processes per gram atom of the active material.

Fig. 7.12a—Solid-radiator parallel-plate chamber (see Fig. 7.12b). 1, grid supported on brass ring. 2, two-mil platinum foil which bears the glycerol tristearate radiator. 3, collecting electrode. 4, guard electrode. 5, high-voltage electrode. 6, lead to the collecting electrode insulated from the base plate with General Electric Kovar-glass seal. 7, high-voltage lead insulated from the plate with a General Electric Kovar-glass seal (a similar lead, not shown in the diagram, provides the connection to the grid). 8, sylphon bellows. 9, structure with keyway for lifting and rotating the radiator in or out of position. The figure shows the radiator lifted out of position. A similar structure supports a blank platinum foil, which may be substituted for the radiator in order to determine the background. 10, soft metal gasket. 11, steel plate, ¼ in. thick. 12, steel shell, ¹⁄₁₆ in. thick. 13, glass insulators. The ends are platinized and soldered to brass caps. 14, cross section of a U-shaped yoke carrying the knurled screw. 15, keyway for rotating radiator.

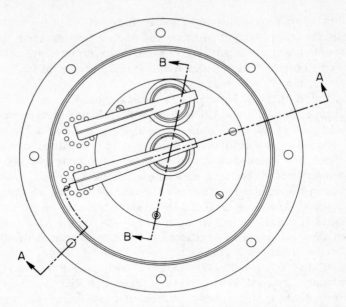

Fig. 7.12b —Solid-radiator parallel-plate chamber (see Sec. 7.12); top view.

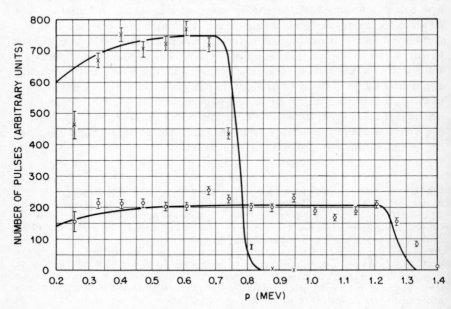

Fig. 7.13 —Differential pulse-height distributions obtained with the chamber with grid shown in Fig. 7.12, irradiated with monoenergetic neutrons of two different energies.

The construction details of the chamber are shown in Fig. 7.14. Extreme care was taken to avoid any heavy material along the path of the neutron beam, so as to minimize the danger of scattering and absorption of neutrons. The chamber walls were made as thin as suitable for the pressure they had to withstand. Only glass insulators were used inside the chamber. The seal between the brass cap and the base plate was made gastight by means of a fuse-wire gasket, so that no materials other than metal and glass were in contact with the gas. The leads to the collecting electrodes and to the high-voltage electrode were shielded from each other by the brass tubes supporting the chamber.

Both argon and xenon, at pressures up to about 9.5 atm, were used as gas fillings. A hot-calcium purifier was permanently attached to the chamber. The chamber was operated between 2,000 and 3,000 volts, depending on the pressure, with the high-voltage electrode negative.

For hydrogenous radiators, glycerol tristearate films of various thicknesses were used. In order to avoid edge effects (see Chap. 3, Sec. 3.7), the diameters of the hydrogenous foil and of the fission foil were chosen so that the ranges of all hydrogen recoils and fission fragments were well within the sensitive volumes of the chambers.

The amplifier used with the recoil chamber had a rise time of 0.5 μsec and a decay time of 20 μsec. The pulses were analyzed with an electronic channel discriminator.

The operation of the chamber was tested with polonium α particles, as described in Sec. 7.12. In addition, the pulse-height distribution of hydrogen recoils was measured for a number of neutron energies. In these measurements the plates of the chamber were perpendicular to the neutron beam with the glycerol tristearate film facing away from the neutron source. Some of the results obtained are reproduced in Fig. 7.15, where the corresponding theoretical curves (see Sec. 7.6) are also given. A channel correction was applied to the theoretical curves. This correction was determined experimentally by means of artificial pulses. The shape of the channel indicated in each curve was found to be approximately trapezoidal; the deviation from a rectangle was, of course, due to noises. The abscissas of the experimental and theoretical curves were matched at the high-energy end near the point of steepest descent, where the influence of the channel is at a minimum. The ordinates were matched a little below the peaks of the curves.

It appears from an inspection of the figures that the agreement between theoretical and experimental pulse-height-distribution curves

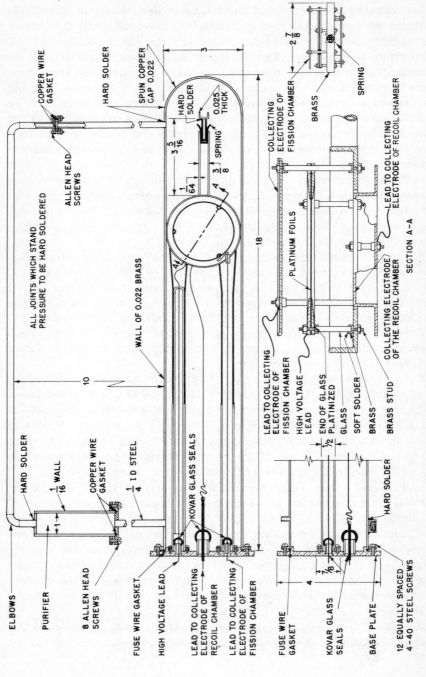

Fig. 7.14—Double recoil and fission chamber (see Sec. 7.13).

is excellent. The deviations at the low-energy end are caused by spurious pulses produced by piling up of argon recoils or of electron recoils from γ rays. The energy at which these effects set in depends, of course, on the experimental conditions. The directionality of the chamber was tested by taking counts with the chamber inverted, i.e., with the glycerol tristearate film perpendicular to the beam but facing the neutron source. Under these conditions, and with neutron energies around 1 mev, the counting rate was found to be about 3 per cent of that recorded in the same neutron beam with the chamber in normal position. The per-cent counting rate increases somewhat with increasing energy and is about 5 per cent around 1.6 mev. Tests were also made with a blank platinum foil in place of the radiator. In most cases, the counting rate with the blank was about 2 per cent of that recorded with a radiator of 173 μg/sq cm thickness.

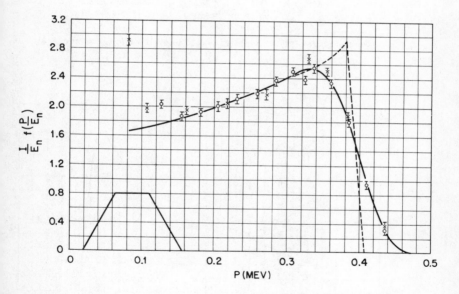

Fig. 7.15a—Figures 7.15a to 7.15e show differential pulse-height distribution curves of hydrogen recoils obtained with the chamber described in Sec. 7.13 by using a monoenergetic neutron beam perpendicular to the radiator. The channel shape is indicated in each graph. Experimental results are represented by dots, circles, or crosses. The vertical bars give the standard statistical errors. Points differently marked refer to different sets of measurements. The dotted lines are theoretical curves without channel correction. The solid lines are theoretical curves with channel corrections. In Fig. 7.15a, E_n = 0.457 mev; t = 67 μg/sq cm; 3 atm of argon.

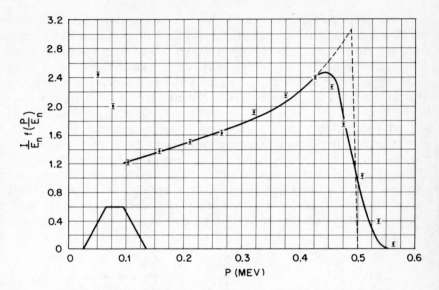

Fig. 7.15b—See legend for Fig. 7.15a. E_n = 0.57 mev; t = 67 μg/sq cm; 3 atm of argon.

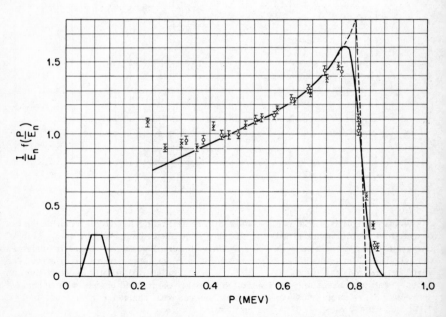

Fig. 7.15c—See legend for Fig. 7.15a. E_n = 1.0 mev; t = 173 μg/sq cm; 6.7 atm of argon.

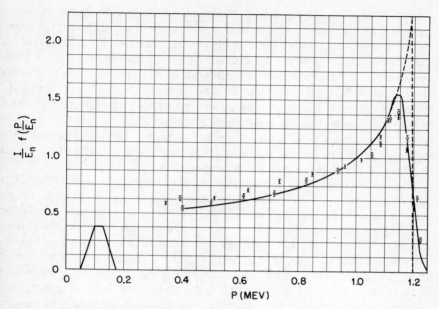

Fig. 7.15d —See legend for Fig. 7.15a. E_n = 1.6 mev; t = 173 μg/sq cm; 9.5 atm of argon.

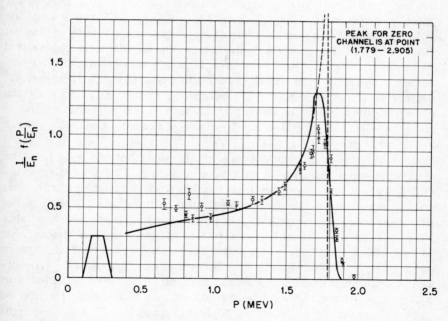

Fig. 7.15e —See legend for Fig. 7.15a. E_n = 2.5 mev; t = 173 μg/sq cm; 9.0 atm of xenon.

7.14 Gas-recoil Cylindrical Chamber. Figure 7.16 shows the construction of a chamber that was used for measuring differential scattering cross sections of light nuclei. The chamber is cylindrical in shape with a thin wire as the collecting electrode. It is built as light as possible in order to minimize inelastic scattering and absorption of neutrons. The chamber can be used with or without gas multiplication. In either case the outer cylinder is kept negative with respect to the wire. The recoils under investigation arise from the gas. In order to reduce the wall effects it is advisable to use a sufficiently high gas pressure so that the maximum range of the recoils is a small fraction of the diameter of the chamber (2.5 cm).

The operation of the chamber was tested by using the $N^{14}(n,p)C^{14}$ reaction, which, with thermal neutrons, gives rise to monoenergetic protons of about 0.6 mev. For this test the chamber was filled with 0.5 atm of nitrogen and 1.5 atm of argon. Under these conditions the range of the 0.6-mev protons was about 0.5 cm. Measurements were taken without gas multiplication and with a gas multiplication of about 35. The pulse amplifier had a rise time of about 0.5 μsec and a decay time of about 20 μsec, so that, when used without gas multiplication, the chamber was operated as an electron-pulse chamber. However, because of the very small diameter of the wire there was not much spread in pulse height, although only the fast part of the pulse was recorded (Chap. 3, Sec. 3.6). Figure 7.17 represents the differential pulse-height distributions as measured with a channel discriminator of the width indicated in the diagram. A theoretical pulse-height-distribution curve for electron pulses was calculated by considering the proton tracks as infinitely short, which involves: (1) neglecting the wall effects; (2) assuming, in the calculation of the electron pulse, that the ionization of each track is concentrated in one point. This theoretical curve, corrected for the channel width, is also represented in Fig. 7.17.

Both of the experimental pulse-height distributions appear to be somewhat wider than might have been expected. The departure of the curve without gas multiplication from the corresponding theoretical curve may possibly be accounted for by wall effects. In the case of the measurements taken with gas multiplication, there was probably some spread in pulse height due to lack of uniformity of the wire or to end effects; or there may have been a small amount of capture since the gas was not purified. After rebuilding the central wire assembly, the measurements with gas multiplication were repeated with a higher pressure in the chamber (0.5 atm of nitrogen and 4 atm of argon). The pulses were analyzed photographically. The pulse-height distribution thus obtained is represented in Fig. 7.18. This curve is

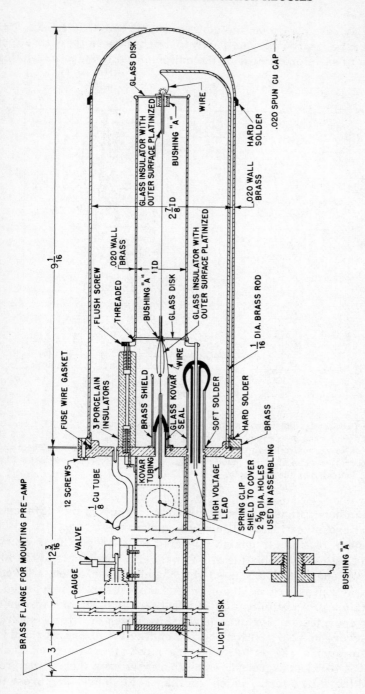

Fig. 7.16—Cylindrical chamber (see Sec. 7.14).

considerably narrower than the corresponding curve (b) in Fig. 7.17. The difference is probably due partly to a decrease in the wall effects and partly to an improvement in the uniformity of the gas multiplication.

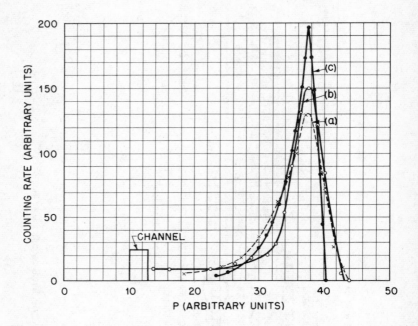

Fig. 7.17—Differential pulse-height distribution curves from the $N^{14}(n,p)C^{14}$ reaction in the cylindrical chamber described in Fig. 7.16. Gas filling 0.5 atm of N_2, 1.5 atm or argon. (a) No gas multiplication. (b) Gas multiplication of about 35. (c) Theoretical curve for operation as an electron-pulse chamber (corrected for channel width). Channel width is indicated by the rectangle.

The chamber was used successfully for measuring the differential scattering cross section of helium and of nitrogen.

A chamber of similar design operated as a proportional counter was used as a neutron-flux meter. For the measurements at the lowest neutron energies (0.03 mev) the chamber was filled with pure hydrogen at a pressure of 10 cm Hg and the voltage was adjusted so as to obtain a gas multiplication of about 50. For the measurements at higher energies, higher pressures of hydrogen or hydrogen-argon mixtures were used. For each neutron energy the pressure should be adjusted in such a way as to strike the most favorable compromise between the γ-ray background, which increases with increasing pressure, and the wall effects, which decrease with increasing pressure.

For a counter of the proportions shown in Fig. 7.16, with the neutron beam parallel to the axis, the best condition is reached when the maximum range of the recoil protons in the counter is of the order of the radius of the counter. In order to minimize the γ-ray background, it is advisable to use, wherever possible, pure hydrogen rather than a hydrogen-argon mixture.

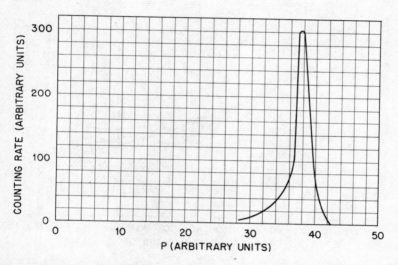

Fig. 7.18—Differential pulse-height distribution curve obtained from the $N^{14}(n,p)C^{14}$ reaction in the cylindrical chamber described in Fig. 7.16. Gas filling 0.5 atm of N_2, 4 atm of argon; gas multiplication about 15. The pulses were analyzed photographically.

A number of pulse-height-distribution curves were measured by exposing the counter to monoenergetic neutrons traveling parallel to the axis. The results obtained with neutrons of 0.5-mev energy are represented in Fig. 7.19, curve c. The pressure was chosen to make the maximum range R of the recoil protons 1.2 times the radius b of the counter. The differential pulse-height-distribution curve, derived theoretically as described in Sec. 7.9 for R = b, is also shown in Fig. 7.19, curve a. In computing this curve, the gradual decrease of the gas multiplication toward the ends of the wires (Chap. 4, Sec. 4.5) was neglected. A calculation which takes into account this effect was carried out, under certain simplifying assumptions, for R = b. The results are given by curve b in Fig. 7.19. Considering the uncertainties in the theoretical calculations and the finite width of the channel discriminator used for the analysis of the pulses, the agreement between the experimental and theoretical results, curves c and b, is reasonably good. The pulse-height-distribution curves are not very sensitive to the ratio R/b. Hence, the comparison between the theoretical and experimental curves is not seriously invalidated by the fact that the value of this ratio was slightly different in the two cases.

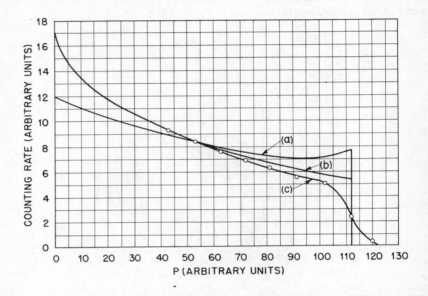

Fig. 7.19 — Differential pulse-height distribution curves of hydrogen recoils for a proportional counter of the type shown in Fig. 7.16; neutron beam parallel to the axis. (a) Calculated for $R_0 = b$, neglecting the change in gas multiplication near the ends of the wire. (b) Calculated for $R_0 = b$, taking into account the change in gas multiplication near the ends of the wire. (c) Observed with 0.5-mev neutrons ($R_0 = 1.2 \ b$).

At lower energies, the experimental curves depart from the theoretical ones and the discrepancy becomes more pronounced as the energy decreases. The reason for such a discrepancy has not yet been determined. It is not impossible that it may be caused, in part or completely, by lack of monochromaticity of the neutron beams used.

7.15   Gas-recoil Proportional Counter. Figure 7.20 illustrates the construction of a chamber that was used as a flux meter for neutrons of low energy (down to 0.035 mev). It is similar in principle to that described in Sec. 7.14. The most interesting feature is the arrangement of the collecting electrode and of the supporting guard electrode. These electrodes are designed to avoid any deformation of the electric field near the ends of the collecting electrode (Chap. 4, Sec. 4.5). The collecting electrode and the guard electrode both consist of sections of hypodermic needles, 0.042-in. OD. They are mechanically connected and electrically insulated by means of glass tubes about 0.025-in. OD, as shown in the detail in Fig. 7.20. The electrical connection

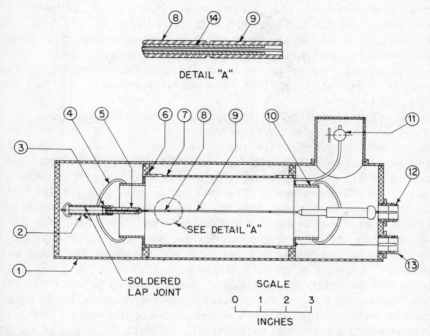

DETAIL "A"

SEE DETAIL "A"

SOLDERED LAP JOINT

SCALE

0   1   2   3

INCHES

Fig. 7.20—Proportional counter (see Sec. 7.15). 1, outer dural case, grounded, 4 in. OD, ¹⁄₁₆-in. wall, 13 in. long. 2, Kovar tube, ⅜ in. OD; it is grounded during operation. 3, Kovar tube, ⅜ in. OD, threaded on the inside. 4, glass. 5, brass rod, threaded on the outside. 6, lucite spacer ring. 7, dural tube, 3 in. OD, ¹⁄₃₂-in. wall in the thinner section. 8, hypodermic needle, 0.042 in. OD; it forms the guard electrode. 9, hypodermic needle, 0.042 in. OD, 4 in. long; it forms the collecting electrode. 10, Kovar tube, ¹⁄₁₆-in. wall; 2¼ in. OD. 11, gas inlet and needle valve. 12, Amphenol connector to the collecting electrode. 13, Amphenol connector to the high-voltage electrode. 14, glass spacer.

to the collecting electrode is made by a thin metal wire that slides through the guard electrode and is soldered to the inside of the collecting electrode.

The walls of the counter and the outer case are made of dural to minimize the possibility of scattering and absorption of neutrons. The Kovar pieces are soldered to the dural end plates with the following technique: first, the Kovar pieces are tinned with soft solder and the dural pieces are covered with Belmont aluminum solder; then each Kovar piece is soldered to the corresponding dural piece with aluminum solder without using flux. The screw connection between pieces 3 and 5 makes it possible to adjust the position of the guard electrodes supporting the collecting electrode before the last Kovar piece is soldered into place. The counter was used only at low energies (down to 0.035 mev), usually with a gas filling of pure hydrogen at 1.5 cm Hg pressure and a gas multiplication around 50. The pulse-height-distribution curves obtained with monoenergetic neutrons are very similar to those obtained at the corresponding energies with the counter described in Sec. 7.14. They do not agree very well with the calculated curves.

7.16   Thick-radiator Electron-pulse Spherical Chamber.   This chamber, whose construction is shown in Fig. 7.21, was designed as a directional detector for relative flux measurements. The radiator is a thick paraffin layer deposited on a section of the removable hemispherical cap and coated with a very thin layer of graphite to make the surface conducting. The chamber is made gastight with neoprene gaskets throughout. The inner electrode assembly is put together, then placed in position and fastened with the nut (a). The gaskets between the collecting electrode and the inner lucite insulator, as well as those between this insulator and the guard electrode, are tightened by means of the nut (b). The gasket between the guard electrode and the outer lucite insulator is tightened by means of the nut (c). The gasket between this insulator and the brass collar is tightened by means of the nut (a). The brass disk on the stem of the collecting electrode is used to reduce the disturbing effect of recoil protons from the lucite insulators. The chamber is filled with argon, and pressures up to 6 atm can be used. It is usually operated at −2,000 volts. A small hole in the chamber wall, covered with an aluminum foil, makes it possible to introduce α particles from a polonium source into the chamber for testing. As already mentioned, the chamber was designed as a directional counter to detect only those neutrons that enter the chamber through the paraffin radiator. The "directionality factor," defined as the ratio between the numbers of counts recorded when the neutrons enter the chamber through the coated and the uncoated surfaces, respectively, is improved by lining the chamber with gold sheet. In this way, a value of about 100 was obtained for the ratio. The counting rate as a function of the angle of incidence of the neutrons is shown in Fig. 7.22. In these measurements the incident neutrons had an energy of 3 mev. The two curves were taken with biases adjusted to count all pulses larger than 1.4 and 1.7 mev, respectively.

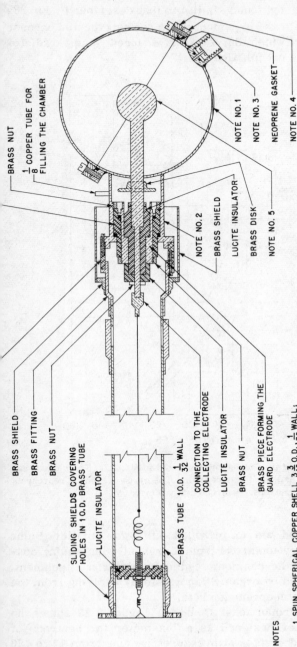

BRASS NUT

$\frac{1}{8}$ COPPER TUBE FOR
FILLING THE CHAMBER

NOTE NO.1

NOTE NO.3

NEOPRENE GASKET

NOTE NO.4

NOTE NO.2

BRASS SHIELD

LUCITE INSULATOR

BRASS DISK

NOTE NO.5

BRASS SHIELD

BRASS FITTING

BRASS NUT

SLIDING SHIELDS COVERING
HOLES IN 1 O.D. BRASS TUBE

LUCITE INSULATOR

BRASS TUBE 1 O.D. $\frac{1}{32}$ WALL

CONNECTION TO THE
COLLECTING ELECTRODE

LUCITE INSULATOR

BRASS NUT

BRASS PIECE FORMING THE
GUARD ELECTRODE

NOTES

1. SPUN SPHERICAL COPPER SHELL $3\frac{3}{16}$ O.D.; $\frac{1}{32}$ WALL;
   IT CONSTITUTES THE HIGH VOLTAGE ELECTRODE.

2. BRASS COLLAR FOR MOUNTING THE HIGH VOLTAGE SPHERICAL SHELL.

3. HOLDER FOR PARTICLE SOURCE. A THIN ALUMINUM FOIL COVERS THE HOLE
   AND THIS WINDOW IS MADE GAS TIGHT WITH A NEOPRENE GASKET.

4. BRASS FLANGES HARD SOLDERED TO THE COPPER SHELL.

5. COLLECTING ELECTRODE MADE OF BRASS STEM $\frac{1}{4}$ IN. DIA.,
   TERMINATING WITH A BRASS SPHERE $\frac{3}{4}$ IN. DIA.

Fig. 7.21 — Spherical chamber (see Sec. 7.16).

The dependence of the counting yield of the chamber on the bias energy was investigated and found similar to that described by Eq. 28a and shown in Fig. 7.6. Close agreement could not be expected because the assumptions under which Eq. 28a was deduced (plane-radiator ion-pulse detection) are not fulfilled.

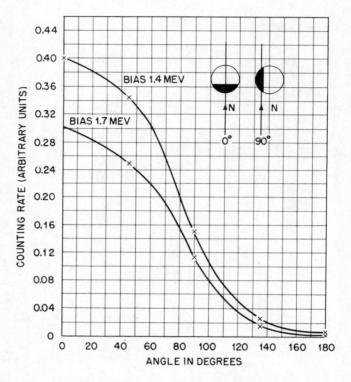

Fig. 7.22 — Angular response of the chamber represented in Fig. 7.21. The black areas represent the portion of the shell lined with paraffin. The arrow marked N represents the direction of the incoming neutrons. Neutron energy 3 mev.

The chamber described was not provided with a gas purifier. Some difficulty during its operation arose from a gradually increasing contamination of the gas of the chamber leading to electron attachment. This was probably caused by organic vapors slowly evolving from the lucite insulators and the neoprene gaskets.

7.17 Thin-radiator Proportional Counter. Figure 7.23 shows the construction of a counter designed as a flux meter for neutrons of low energies. Argon and krypton at pressures ranging from 12 to 170

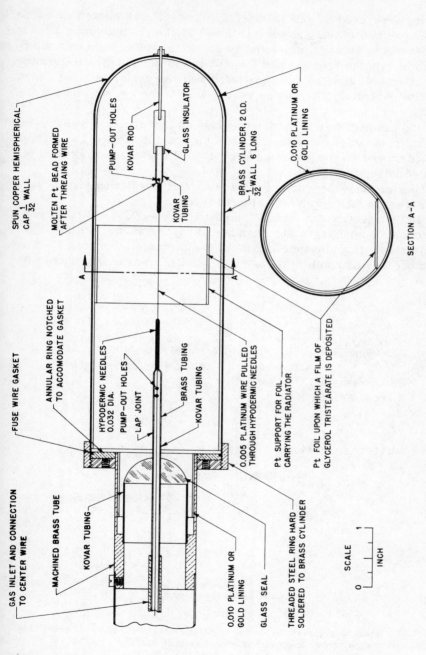

Fig. 7.23—Thin-radiator proportional counter (see Sec. 7.17).

cm Hg were used as gas fillings. The voltage was chosen so as to obtain gas multiplications between 5 and 50. The radiator was a layer of glycerol tristearate deposited by distillation in vacuum on a platinum foil. Its thickness varied from 60 to 390 μg/sq cm. The counter was operated with the case grounded and the center wire at a high positive potential. The pulses were taken off the center wire by capacity coupling.

If the gas pressure is sufficiently high so that practically all recoil tracks from the radiator terminate in the gas, the yield of the counter should depend on the neutron energy E_n and the bias energy B as indicated in Fig. 7.1.

Experiments were carried out to test this prediction and the results were in fair agreement with the theory.

7.18 Integrating Gas-recoil Chamber. Figure 7.24 shows the construction of an integrating chamber designed at the British T. A. Project for flux measurements of monoenergetic neutrons. The chamber is filled with ethylene (C_2H_4) and the walls are coated with

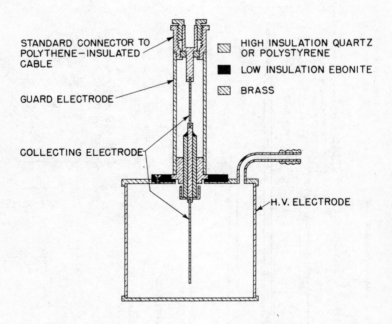

Fig. 7.24 — Integrating gas-recoil ionization chamber (see Sec. 7.18). Vacuum seals on the body of the chamber made with low-melting-point wax.

paraffin wax to a thickness larger than the maximum range of the recoil protons. The surface of the wax is made conducting by evaporating silver to a thickness of 0.2 mg/sq cm. The paraffin wax used had the composition $(CH_2)_n$, i.e., it contained carbon and hydrogen in the same proportion as the gas filling of the chamber. Under these circumstances the wall effects are eliminated when the instrument is used as an integrating chamber. In other words, the ionization per unit volume of the gas is the same as if the dimensions of the chamber were infinitely large compared with the range of the recoil protons. The ionization current produced by the hydrogen recoils I_H is then given by Eq. 29, which may be rewritten as

$$I_H = \phi A \eta_H \sigma_H(E_n) \frac{E_n}{2} \frac{e}{W_0}$$

where A is the volume of the chamber; ϕ is the neutron flux density, i.e., the number of neutrons per second per square centimeter; η_H is the number of hydrogen atoms per cubic centimeter of the gas; and σ_H is the total scattering cross section of hydrogen.

To the ionization current produced by the hydrogen recoils, add that produced by the carbon recoils, which can be expressed as

$$I_c = \phi A \eta_c \sigma_c(E_n)(E)_{av} \frac{e}{W_0}$$

where η_c is the number of carbon atoms per cubic centimeter of the gas, $\sigma_c(E_n)$ is the total scattering cross section of carbon, and $(E)_{av}$ is the average energy of the carbon recoils. Because of some uncertainty in the values of σ_c and $(E)_{av}$, the relation between I_c and ϕ is not so well-known as that between I_H and ϕ. On the other hand, I_c is small compared with I_H since the carbon cross section is considerably smaller than that of hydrogen, so this uncertainty does not introduce any appreciable source of error.

Very often neutrons are accompanied by γ rays. With a pulse chamber the γ-ray pulses can be biased off, but this cannot be done with an integrating chamber. It is possible, however, to separate the effects of neutrons from those of γ rays by determining simultaneously the ionization current for the chamber described above and for a second identical chamber in which all hydrogen has been replaced with deuterium. The substitution of deuterium for hydrogen in an ionization chamber does not change the sensitivity of the chamber for γ rays (this was experimentally verified). It does, however, change its sensitivity to neutrons. Hence, the difference of ionization currents is proportional to the neutron flux.

Assuming there is isotropic scattering of neutrons on deuterons in the center-of-gravity system, the difference ΔI of ionization currents is related to the neutron-flux density n by the equation

$$\Delta I = \phi A \ \frac{E_n}{2} \ \frac{e}{W_0} \ n \ \ [\sigma_H(E_n) - {}^8\!/_9 \sigma_D(E_n)]$$

where $\sigma_D(E_n)$ is the total scattering cross section of deuterons, n is the number of hydrogen or deuterium atoms per cubic centimeter, and $\frac{1}{2}({}^8\!/_9 E_n)$ represents the average energy of the deuterium recoils. It may be pointed out that the assumption of isotropic scattering of neutrons on deuterons, which enters in the evaluation of the average energy, is somewhat uncertain.

7.19 Coincidence Proportional Counter. Figure 7.25 illustrates the construction of a detector used as an absolute neutron-flux meter. It consists essentially of two proportional counters. The recoil protons, ejected from the paraffin radiator, are collimated by diaphragms 2 and 3. Only those recoils are recorded that traverse both proportional counters and produce simultaneous pulses. The ratio of the number of recoils recorded to the total number of recoils generated in the radiator is determined by the solid angle defined by the diaphragms. The effective area of the radiator is determined by another diaphragm (1) placed directly in front of the radiator.

The radiator consists of a paraffin film evaporated on a metal disk. Tank argon, at pressures ranging from 1 to 10 cm Hg, was used as a gas filling. Aluminum and collodion foils of different thicknesses, mounted on two disks, can be placed along the path of the recoil protons to determine their range. From the range of recoil protons the energy of the incident neutrons can be calculated. The disks carrying the absorbing foils can be rotated from the outside through ground joints. The thin wire rings on both sides of the absorbing foils were used to shield the two counters electrically from one another. This was found necessary because otherwise the operation of the counters was modified by insertion of an aluminum foil between them. Measurements of the coincidence counting rate vs. bias showed the existence of flat "plateaus," indicating that all the pulses produced by the hydrogen recoils in the proportional counters had sizes greater than a certain value well above the background noises.

The instrument described did not prove very reliable as an absolute neutron-flux meter. However, it is likely that a satisfactory instrument could be built on the same principle by improving the design of the counters. Multiple-wire proportional counters (Chap. 4, Sec. 4.7) might prove particularly suitable in this arrangement.

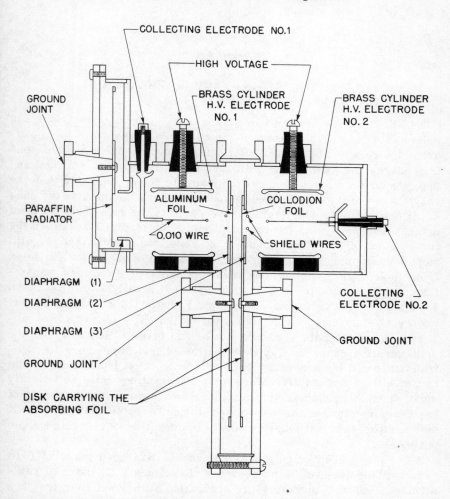

Fig. 7.25—Coincidence proportional counter (see Sec. 7.19). Black areas represent hard-rubber insulators. Counters are made gastight with glyptal.

Chapter 8

DETECTORS OF (n,α) AND (n,p) REACTIONS

8.1 <u>Neutron Spectroscopy by Means of (n,α) or (n,p) Reactions</u>. In principle it is possible to use the (n,α) and (n,p) reactions for measuring the energy distribution of a neutron beam. At any given neutron energy the total energy released in the reaction is constant and depends on the neutron energy in a simple form, provided that the reaction products are emitted in the ground state, which is the case in many reactions. The total energy, which is the sum of the incident neutron energy E_n and the reaction energy Q, is divided between the two outgoing charged particles. If the reactions occurs in a gas with sufficient stopping power to prevent the escape of any of the particles from the counting volume, the resulting pulses are of sizes proportional to $E_n + Q$. Since Q is constant and usually known, such an arrangement provides an almost ideal method for measuring the energy of monoenergetic neutrons for which $(E_n + Q) > 0$. (For accurate measurements Q should not be too large.) However, for the determination of the energy distribution of non-monoenergetic neutrons it would be necessary to know the energy dependence of the cross section accurately. Moreover, all reactions with sufficiently small Q exhibit pronounced resonances, which make interpretation of the experimental results even more difficult. Table 8.1 gives a list of reactions that have been under consideration for spectroscopic purposes.

8.2 <u>Flux Measurements</u>. Extensive use has been made of (n,α) reactions for detecting slow neutrons. Reactions 1, 2, and 3 in Table 8.1 have positive Q and therefore occur also at thermal energies. The reaction $B(n,\alpha)$ (reaction 2) is most commonly used because the cross section is very large and, furthermore, is known to obey the $1/v$ law in the low-energy region ($E_n < 500$ ev). The value of the cross section for $v_n = 2,200$ m/sec is $730 \pm 9 \times 10^{-24}$ sq cm for the natural isotopic mixture of B^{10} and B^{11}, and therefore is $3,960 \times 10^{-24}$ sq cm for pure B^{10}. Reactions 1 and 3 have considerably lower cross sections than the reaction B(n,α). In the case of reaction 1, the materials are not so easy to handle as boron. For these reasons the following sections are confined to the discussion of boron detectors. Such detectors have been used not only to measure small neutron flux but also to detect fast neutrons after they have been slowed down by a suitable moderator.

Table 8.1

Reaction	Q, mev	Remarks
(1) $_3Li^6 + _0n^1 \rightarrow _2He^4 + _1H^3$	+4.63	Resonance at $E_n = 0.27$ mev, Q high, σ very large at $E_n = 0$
(2) $_5B^{10} + _0n^1 \rightarrow _2He^4 + _3Li^7$	+2.34 and 2.78	No resonances, Q fairly large, σ very large at $E_n = 0$
(3) $_7N^{14} + _0n^1 \rightarrow _1H^1 + _6C^{14}$	+0.60	σ shows sharp resonance at 0.55, 0.7, and 1.45 mev
(4) $_7N^{14} + _0n^1 \rightarrow _2He^4 + _5B^{11}$	−0.28	σ shows resonance at 1.5 mev

The B(n,α) reaction has been studied extensively by Bower, Bretscher, and Gilbert.* The reaction is not monoenergetic, but for thermal neutrons leads only rarely to the ground state of Li^7. The majority of the disintegrations result in the well-known excited state of Li^7 at 0.44 mev. The ranges of the particles are given as 0.7 cm for the α particles and 0.4 cm for the Li nuclei. Since the Q value of the reaction leading to the excited state of Li is 2.34 mev, the Li nucleus, for thermal neutrons, carries 0.85 mev.

Solid boron can be used as well as gaseous compounds. The gaseous filling consists most frequently of BF_3, which is a comparatively stable compound. Considerable difficulties are encountered in purifying the gas sufficiently to prevent electron capture, especially at pressures greater than 1 atm. Careful distillation from frozen (−127°C) commercial BF_3 improves the gas considerably in this respect, apparently by removing substances such as HF, which capture the electrons. However, the best BF_3 fillings were obtained by thermal decomposition of $C_6H_5N_2BF_4$. The difficulties of purification are avoided by coating the electrodes of the detector with thin films of solid boron and filling the chamber with an inert gas such as argon or a mixture of argon and CO_2. The boron films can be prepared by

*Proc. Cambridge Phil. Soc., 34: 290 (1938).

decomposing borane (B_2C_6) on heated foils of tungsten or tantalum. The disadvantage of this type of detector as compared with the gaseous ones is the fact that in order to obtain high counting yields a large number of foils must be used since the range of the reaction particles is very small. For absolute measurements the use of solid films is advisable because the amount of irradiated material can be determined very accurately.* The use of B^{10} isotope obviously increases the sensitivity of both types of detectors by about a factor of 5 as compared with detectors using the natural isotopic mixture of 81.6 per cent inactive B^{11} and 18.4 per cent B^{10}.

For absolute measurements of a slow neutron flux, the neutron energy must, of course, be known, since the cross section of the $B(n,\alpha)$ reaction varies rapidly with energy. Corrections have to be applied for the finite film thickness in the case of solid films, and wall corrections must be made in the case of gas-filled detectors.

Consider first the case of a parallel-plate ion-pulse chamber with a solid boron film of finite thickness t deposited on the high-voltage electrode. The detection efficiency F(B) (number of counts divided by the number of disintegrations) is given by

$$F(B) = \frac{1}{2} \left\{ 1 - \frac{t}{2 [R_0 - R(B)]} \right\} \qquad (1)$$

where R_0 is the range of the emitted α particle and R(B) is the range of an α particle of energy B. Both ranges are to be measured in the material of the film (appendix, Sec. 6). In this formula it is assumed that all α particles have the same energy, that $[R_0 - R(B)] \geq t$, and that the pulses from the lithium nuclei are not counted (B > 0.85 mev). The formula does not apply rigorously to the case of an electron-pulse chamber. However, it applies approximately if the range of the α particles in the chamber is sufficiently small and the value of B is sufficiently low. If the bias energy is lower than 0.85 mev so that Li pulses are also counted, the expression for the detection efficiency becomes

$$F(B) = 1 - \frac{t}{4} \left[\frac{1}{R_{01} - R_1(B)} + \frac{1}{R_{02} - R_2(B)} \right] \qquad (2)$$

where the subscript 1 refers to the α particle and the subscript 2 to the Li. Again this formula holds only if $[R_{02} - R_2(B)] \geq t$.

---

*Tungsten as a carrier foil has proved to be unsuitable for such measurements since boron apparently diffuses into the metal. This does not seem to occur in the case of tantalum foils.

Consider next a cylindrical chamber of radius b filled with a boron-containing gas and operated as an ion-pulse chamber. The computation of the exact expression for the detection efficiency is very complicated if the finite range of the Li recoil is taken into account. Furthermore, it cannot be carried out without an exact knowledge of the range-energy relation of very slow Li particles. Thus it is assumed that the ionization from the Li recoil is confined to a very small region around the origin of the disintegration. This assumption is rather crude since the range of the Li recoil according to Bower, Bretscher, and Gilbert is about $\frac{4}{11}$ of the total range of the two particles. It appears, however, from the photometric traces of cloud-chamber tracks that most of the ionization of the Li recoil occurs close to the point of origin of the disintegration. The contribution of the Li, in the case of thermal neutrons, shall be taken as equal to 0.85 mev. Under these assumptions the detection efficiency becomes

$$F(B) = 1 - \frac{r(B)}{2b} \qquad (3)$$

where $r(B)$ is that portion of the range of the α particle (measured from the point of origin) which it must spend in the sensitive volume in order to produce, together with the Li recoil, a pulse equal to the bias energy. If R_0 is the range of the α particle, $E(R)$ is the energy corresponding to a certain range R, B is the bias energy, and E_{Li} is the energy of the Li recoil, then

$$B - E_{Li} = E(R_0) - E[R_0 - r(B)] \qquad (4)$$

In deriving Eq. 3 it is assumed that $r(B) \ll b$.

In most cases the best procedure to obtain the counting rate at zero bias energy consists in determining the number of counts as a function of the bias and extrapolating linearly to zero bias. This procedure is satisfactory if the measurements extend to a sufficiently low bias.

8.3 Boron Chamber of High Sensitivity. Figure 8.1 shows the construction of a highly sensitive boron chamber that can be used for detecting neutrons of all energies by slowing them down in paraffin in order to increase the cross section for the B(n,α) reaction. The chamber consists of a cylindrical vessel with a central electrode supported by guard electrodes. It is embedded in a 50-cm cube of paraffin. The diameters of the inner and outer electrodes are $2\frac{1}{4}$ and $4\frac{3}{8}$ in., respectively. The gas filling consists of BF_3 prepared by decomposition of $C_6H_5N_2BF_4$ at a pressure of 74.6 cm Hg. The

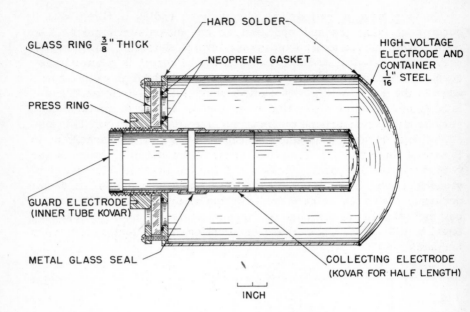

GLASS RING $\frac{3}{8}$ " THICK

HARD SOLDER

NEOPRENE GASKET

HIGH-VOLTAGE
ELECTRODE AND
CONTAINER
$\frac{1}{16}$ " STEEL

PRESS RING

GUARD ELECTRODE
(INNER TUBE KOVAR)

METAL GLASS SEAL

COLLECTING ELECTRODE
(KOVAR FOR HALF LENGTH)

INCH

Fig. 8.1 — High-sensitivity boron trifluoride chamber.

chamber is connected to an amplifier of 0.2 μsec rise time and 20 μsec resolving time. Figure 8.2 shows the dependence of the counting rate on chamber voltage. The drop of the curve below 3 kv shows that a considerable fraction of electrons is captured even in a gas so pure. Figure 8.3 shows the bias curve at 4-kv chamber voltage.

For all neutron energies the highest sensitivity is obtained when the source is placed in the cylindrical cavity of the inner electrode. However, the sensitivity is then markedly dependent on the energy of the primary neutrons. Thus source-strength comparisons are possible only by a careful calibration at various neutron energies. If the source is moved away from the chamber in a plane perpendicular to the axis, the sensitivity decreases (see Fig. 8.4). Since the decrease is more rapid for less energetic neutrons, there is a region (13 cm from the axis) where the counting yield depends only slightly on the energy. From Fig. 8.4 it is evident that the maximum sensitivity, defined as the number of counts divided by the number of emitted neutrons, is of the order of a few per cent, in fair agreement with an estimated value. The detector has been used to measure the strength of very weak sources. The background is about 15 counts per minute.

8.4 **BF$_3$ Counter Arrangement of High Sensitivity.** The apparatus consists of 12 BF$_3$ proportional counters arranged with their axes on

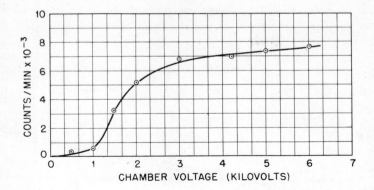

Fig. 8.2 — Counting rate vs. chamber voltage for the boron trifluoride chamber shown in Fig. 1.

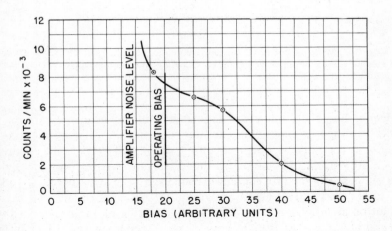

Fig. 8.3 — Counting rate vs. bias for the boron trifluoride chamber shown in Fig. 8.1. Voltage, 4,000 volts; pressure, 746 mm Hg.

a cylinder of 9-in. diameter. They are embedded in a cylindrical block of paraffin 18 in. in diameter and 16 in. in length, with a central cylindrical opening of 5-in. diameter in which the source is placed. The counters are 2 in. in diameter and 12 in. long, and are of simple construction. The central electrode is 1-mil Kovar wire supported by glass insulators. No guard electrodes are used, which makes careful cleaning and drying of the insulators necessary. The counters are filled with B^{10} enriched BF_3 containing 70 per cent B^{10} to a pressure of 600 mm Hg. With a polonium-beryllium neutron source in the center of the paraffin block, the sensitivity is 13 per cent when the counters are connected in parallel and operated at $-2,600$ volts.

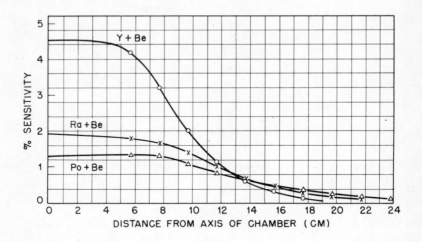

Fig. 8.4 — Sensitivity of boron trifluoride chamber (Fig. 8.1) vs. distance of source from chamber, in a plane perpendicular to the axis of the chamber. The various curves are taken with sources of different average primary neutron energies.

Figures 8.5 and 8.6 show the dependence of the counting rate on the counter voltage at fixed bias, and the dependence of counting rate on the bias at the normal counter voltage of $-2,600$ volts. The resolving time of the amplifier used for these measurements was 0.5 μ sec. Both curves exhibit flat regions around the operating point. In addition to its very high counting yield, this arrangement has a high resolution and is therefore capable of counting at high rates without appreciable loss. At 40,000 counts per second in the 12 counters, the loss is only 5.5 per cent. This quantity was measured in the usual way by comparing the counting rates of two different sources, measured individually, with the observed counting rate when the sources were placed simultaneously in the detector. From the measured loss and the resolving time of the amplifier, it is apparent that the total resolving time of the arrangement is determined mainly by the counters.

8.5 Flat-response Counters. The detectors described in the two preceding sections have sensitivities that depend very strongly on the energy of the primary neutrons. Several attempts have been made to find an arrangement of paraffin surrounding a boron detector such that the number of boron disintegrations is proportional to the number

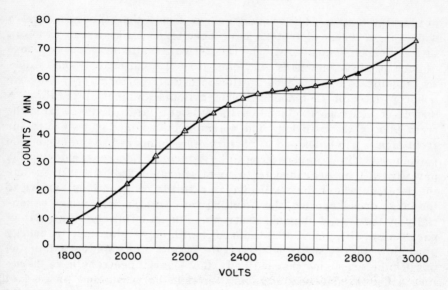

Fig. 8.5 — Counting rate vs. counter voltage of high-sensitivity boron trifluoride proportional counters.

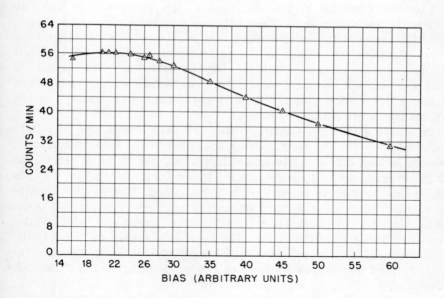

Fig. 8.6 — Counting rate vs. bias at −2,600 volts counter voltage of high-sensitivity
boron trifluoride proportional counters.

of primary source neutrons and independent of their energies over a wide range. These detectors have been termed long boron counters or flat-response counters. The theoretical treatment of the response of such an arrangement is very complicated. Qualitatively the following arguments might serve to illustrate their performance. Suppose a boron detector is embedded in a cylindrical block of paraffin. A source of neutrons is placed on the axis at a large distance from the front face of the cylinder. The detector is assumed to extend to the front face of the block and to be very long compared to the mean free path in paraffin of any neutron to be detected. Neutrons entering the paraffin will be degraded to thermal energies and will diffuse into the detector where they will give rise to $B(n,\alpha)$ reactions. Owing to the large cross section, the counting rate will be determined essentially by the flux of thermal neutrons. For an infinitely large slab of paraffin the efficiency would increase with increasing neutron energy since low-energy neutrons penetrate only a short distance into the paraffin before being thermalized. Low-energy neutrons have therefore a better chance of escaping through the front face (instead of passing through the boron detector) than neutrons that were originally of higher energy and are therefore thermalized at a greater distance from the front face. The reason for this is twofold. At higher energies, more collisions are required for thermalization, and the collision cross section is smaller than at low energies. In order to minimize the dependence of the efficiency on the energy, the dimensions of the paraffin must be such that the thermalized fast neutrons have an increased chance to escape from the paraffin. Obviously it is not possible to accomplish this for all energies from thermal to several million electron volts. However, arrangements have been found which exhibit rather flat response curves over energy regions of several million electron volts.

Among the various constructions, two have shown the best flat-response curves. The first one (the so-called "8-inch-long counter"), shown in Fig. 8.7, consists of a paraffin cylinder 12 in. in length and 8 in. in diameter. Along its axis a BF_3 proportional counter 1 in. in diameter and 8 in. in active length is embedded. It protrudes slightly over the front face of the paraffin but is protected from direct thermal neutrons by a cadmium shield. The counter is electrically shielded by an aluminum tube. For insulation the space between the counter wall and the shield is filled with ceresin wax. The central electrode of the counter consists of a Kovar wire of 10-mil diameter. The counter is filled with enriched (80 per cent B^{10}) BF_3 to a pressure of 25 cm Hg. With $-2,700$ volts applied to the wall, a gas amplification of about 10 is obtained. The sensitivity versus neutron energy is represented in Fig. 8.8. Measurements were taken with the source

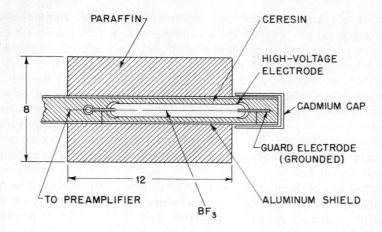

Fig. 8.7 — Detail of 8-in. flat-response counter.

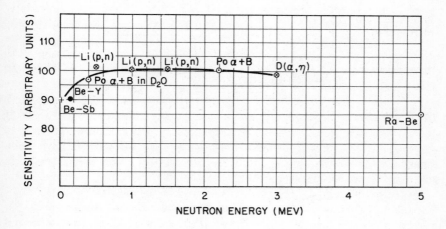

Fig. 8.8 — Sensitivity curve of 8-in. flat-response counter.

of neutrons on the axis of the detector 1 m from the front face. The arrangement was in the center of a room 20×15 ft, and 50 in. above the floor so as to minimize the effect of scattering and degrading of the neutrons by floor and walls. Even with this arrangement it is believed that 15 per cent of the counted neutrons were scattered. The absolute sensitivity is about one count for every 10^5 neutrons emitted by a spherically symmetrical source. The most reliable points of the sensitivity curves are those taken with the Li(p,n) and D(D,n) sources.

The flux of these sources was determined by U^{235} fission counts. Their energies are exactly known (points at 0.5, 1.0, 1.5, and 3 mev). Similarly reliable are the points at 0.16 mev and 0.023 mev, which were taken with (γ,n) sources of known strength of (Be + Y) and (Be + Sb), respectively. For the points at 0.4 mev, 2.2 mev, and 5 mev, sources with a complex neutron spectrum were used to which certain average energy is ascribed. These points are therefore open to some doubt. This is particularly true for the point taken with the radium-beryllium source. It is estimated, furthermore, that the response at thermal energy of the neutrons is around 70 in the units used on Fig. 8.8.

A considerable improvement of the response was achieved with the arrangement shown in Fig. 8.9. Here the counter is shielded with an additional layer of paraffin separated from the inner part by a boron

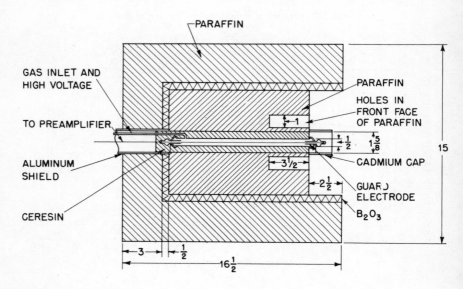

Fig. 8.9—Detail of 15-in. shielded flat-response counter.

carbide or boron trioxide shield. This extra layer reduces the number of counts caused by stray neutrons to about 5 per cent when the source is again placed 1 m from the front face. The sensitivity for low-energy neutrons is increased by drilling a set of holes into the front face of the paraffin cylinder. These holes give the low-energy neutrons a better chance of entering the boron detector before being reflected back through the front face. Eight holes 1 in. in diameter and 3½ in. deep are drilled parallel to the axis of the paraffin cylinder with their centers on a circle of 3½ in. diameter. The boron trifluoride counter used in this arrangement has a diameter of ½ in. and active length of 10½ in. It is otherwise similar to the one used in the preceding arrangement. The dependence of the sensitivity on the neutron energy is shown in Fig. 8.10. The thermal-energy point was measured with photo neutrons from (Be + Sb) degraded strongly by a

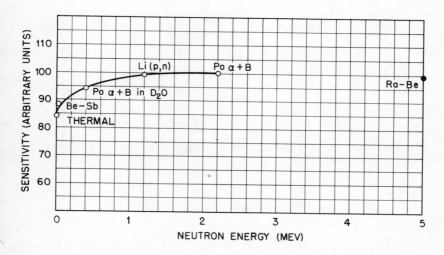

Fig. 8.10—Sensitivity of 15-in. shielded flat-response counter at different neutron energies.

layer of heavy water. The point at 0.023 mev was obtained with the same source without degradation, and the point at 1.2 mev with a Li(p,n) source, the flux of which was determined by a U^{235} fission detector. These points are therefore very reliable. The points at 0.4 mev, 2.2 mev, and 5 mev (Ra + Be) are taken with a complex neutron spectrum and are therefore questionable.

8.6 Solid-boron Radiator Chamber. The chamber is of parallel-plate type with the boron-covered foil on the negative high-voltage electrode. The electrode separation is 0.4 cm and the diameter of the electrodes 1.6 cm. The chamber is filled with argon at about 3 atm pressure and operates with a collecting voltage of between 100 and 200 volts. The boron is deposited on a tantalum foil by thermal decomposition of B_2C_6. The deposit has a diameter of 1.4 cm and has a thickness of about 25 μg/sq cm, which is considerably less than the range of either the α particles or the Li recoils. The bias curve obtained with this chamber is shown in Fig. 8.11. The plateau is sufficiently flat, and the correction for finite thickness given by Eqs. 1 and 2 can be applied to determine the counting rate at zero bias.

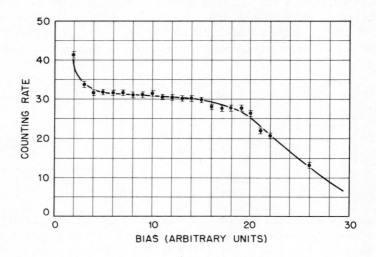

Fig. 8.11 — Bias curve of boron-foil counter.

8.7 Absolute BF$_3$ Detectors. Two detectors with gaseous boron compounds suitable for absolute flux measurements are shown in Figs. 8.12 and 8.14. Their common characteristic is the accurately known volume in which the counted pulses originate.

In the cylindrical chamber (Fig. 8.12) there is only a small region where it is uncertain whether or not detectable pulses originate. This region is the space where the collecting electrode passes from the opening of the high-voltage electrode through the guard electrode. The counting volume was determined by filling the chamber with water. The counting rate C is related to the neutron-flux density ϕ by the equation

$$C = \phi A \sigma n \tag{5}$$

where n is the number of B^{10} atoms per cubic centimeter, σ is the disintegration cross section, and A is the active volume. For the chamber shown in Fig. 8.12, the counting volume is 17.86 cu cm. The volume of the uncertain region is 0.31 cu cm, or less than 2 per cent of the main counting volume. The corners of the counting volume are carefully rounded, a precaution that greatly reduces the wall effects.

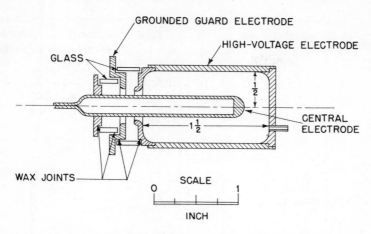

Fig. 8.12 — Definite-volume boron trifluoride ionization chamber.

Figure 8.13 shows bias curves obtained with this chamber at different pressures and suitable collecting voltages. The various curves were taken with the chamber in the same neutron flux. The numbers attached to each curve give the counting rates per unit pressure at equal temperature, and it is apparent that within an error of about 1 per cent these numbers are equal. The counting rates for zero bias were not calculated but were obtained by linear extrapolation of the observed curves. Since the slopes are quite small, this procedure seems to be adequate. A calculation of the correction due to wall effects for this type of chamber would be very inaccurate.

In the proportional counter (see Fig. 8.14) the counting volume is limited by two disks of semiconducting material carrying sufficient current to prevent accumulation of charges. The disks establish an electric field that varies radially at the boundary of the counting volume in the same manner as in the central region of the counter. In this way the usual end effects of proportional counters (see Chap. 4, Sec. 4.5) are avoided. The disks consist of soft glass, coated with Aquadag and metalized on the outer edge in order to ensure contact with the counter wall. The central 10-mil platinum wire is fused into very small holes in the glass disks. The technique of drilling small holes into the disks is as follows:

The glass plate is cemented onto a rubber diaphragm covering a vessel connected to a rubber squeeze ball. In this way the disk can be pressed gently and with uniform pressure against the drill. The latter consists of a short piece of tungsten wire, the diameter of which is slightly less than that required for the hole. It is soldered into a

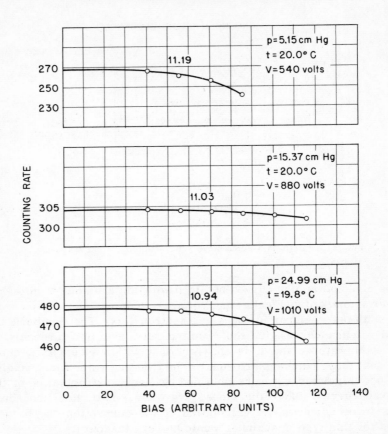

Fig. 8.13 — Bias curves of definite-volume BF_3 ionization chamber. Curves are taken at different pressures. The numbers accompanying each curve give the counting rate at unit pressure and 0°C.

round piece of brass, which is clamped into a chuck driven by an air turbine or a suitable high-speed electric drill rotating at about 7,000 rpm. Six-hundred-mesh carborundum with water serves as a grinding agent. With this arrangement, holes as small as 3 mils in diameter can be drilled. In order to fuse the platinum wire into the glass, the wire is threaded through the hole of the disk, which is then placed into a furnace at the annealing temperature of the glass. The fusing is accomplished by passing a current of suitable strength through the wire so that the glass melts onto the wire.

By shooting α particles radially into the counter through mica windows, it was found that the gas multiplication is very constant up to a distance of 1 mm from the disks. Figure 8.15 shows bias curves

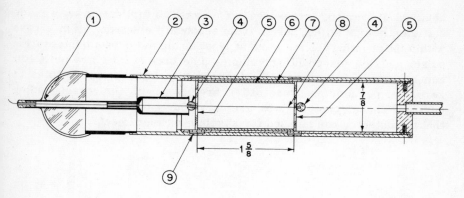

Fig. 8.14—Definite-volume boron trifluoride proportional counter. 1, Kovar-glass seal. 2, outer shell. 3, protecting sleeve for collecting electrode. 4, glass beads. 5, glass disks (edges metalized or painted with Aquadag). 6, spacer. 7, inner shell. 8, collecting electrode (0.01-in. platinum wire). 9, vent holes.

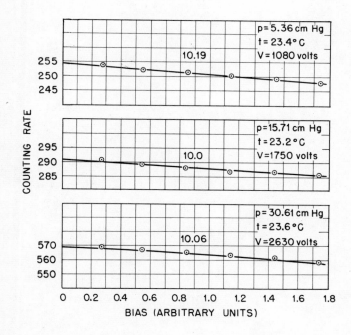

Fig. 8.15—Bias curves of definite-volume BF$_3$ counter. Curves are taken at different pressures. The numbers accompanying each curve give the counting rate at unit pressure and 0°C.

obtained at various pressures. The gas multiplication was made sufficiently high so that pulses from secondary electrons from γ rays within the counting volume were at least as big as boron-disintegration pulses outside the counting volume. The bias curves are quite flat and can easily be extrapolated to zero bias. The counting rates at zero bias per unit pressure at 0°C are given with the corresponding curves. These counting rates are very nearly the same. This shows that the detector can be used for absolute measurements.

Chapter 9

FISSION DETECTORS

9.1 <u>Introduction</u>. The main purposes for which fission detectors are used are:

1. Measurement of the rate of fissions in a given neutron flux for the determination of the fission cross section; measurement of the rate of fissions in a material with known cross section for the determination of flux of monoenergetic neutrons. In both cases it is important to know accurately the amount of fissionable material and to count quantitatively the number of fissions occurring in the material.

2. Relative measurements of neutron flux of sources with identical spectra. In this case it is desirable to have a detector of high counting yield, but the absolute value of this quantity does not have to be known. The various fissionable materials offer the possibility of constructing detectors with different yields for different neutron energies since the materials have different threshold energies.

3. Investigation of the energy distribution of the fission fragments. Detectors for this purpose are very similar in construction to the ones used for the study of α-particle spectra.

In most cases the fissionable material is used in the form of thin foils. Since the mean range of the fission fragments is only about 2.1 cm in air it is evident that only very thin layers of material can be used for absolute detectors. This makes it necessary to spread the material over large areas if detectors of high counting yields are desired. The use of a gaseous fissionable compound would avoid this difficulty. Uranium hexafluoride (UF_6) might be suitable, but unfortunately experiments with this gas have not been successful. Electron collection, which is of prime importance because of the necessity of achieving short resolving times (see below), could not be obtained in this gas. Moreover, the highly corrosive nature of UF_6 causes difficulties with common insulators.

The fission pulses originating from a solid deposit of fissionable material show, of course, a wide spread in energy, ranging from zero to about 110 mev. This is due partly to the natural spread from about 40 to 110 mev, and partly to the energy loss that fragments undergo in passing through the fissionable material. Nevertheless it is possible to obtain bias curves that show (below about half the maximum energy) a rather flat plateau. Since two fission fragments result from every fission process, the number of fission pulses observed within a solid angle of 2π is equal to the number of fissions produced in the material.

In every fission detector, the fission pulses are superimposed over a background of very numerous α particles. It is therefore important that the resolving time of a fission detector and of its amplifier be made as short as possible in order to avoid piling up several α-particle pulses to a height comparable with a fission pulse. Since the α particles have energies of around 4 mev, a pile-up of about five α-particles pulses will still permit observation of a rather large fraction of the fission pulses. This consideration usually sets an upper limit on the total amount of material that can be put into a detector. An approximate estimate of the pile-up of α-particle pulses can be obtained from the following formula (see the appendix, Sec. 11):

$$C(n) = \frac{n_0}{1 + n_0\tau} \frac{(n_0\tau)^{n-1}}{(n-1)!} e^{-n_0\tau} \tag{1}$$

where $C(n)$ is the number of counts per unit time containing n unresolved pulses and n_0 is the true number of pulses per unit time. The pulses are assumed to be of rectangular shape and of a duration τ. It may be pointed out that n pulses of height P do not necessarily give a pulse height nP. The resulting size depends largely on the frequency response of the amplifier, since the pulse height nP is only reached during a time smaller than τ. For practical purposes Eq. 1 holds only approximately since in most cases the pulses will be of an exponential character. However, it gives the right order of magnitude if τ is taken equal to the resolving time as defined in Chap. 3, Sec. 3.3.

Whenever it is desirable to have as much fissionable material as possible in a chamber, the pile-up of α particles can be effectively reduced by adjusting the dimensions of the detector and the pressure of the gas so that the fission fragments spend in the sensitive volume only a fraction of their range. Since, in contrast to the behavior of α particles, the highest energy loss per unit path length occurs for fission fragments at the beginning of the track, and since the range of the α particles is roughly twice the range of the fission fragments, the above arrangement leads to a large increase in the relative size of fission pulses as compared to α-particle pulses. An additional improvement consists in placing over the fissionable material a plate in which a large number of suitable holes are drilled. In this way the fission fragments and α particles are collimated to a certain extent and are prevented from entering the chamber at small angles with respect to the electrode. Even in a shallow parallel-plate chamber, most of the particles emitted at a grazing angle would have all or nearly all their path within the counting volume and would therefore give an unfavorable ratio of fission-pulse to α-pulse height.

Since, in every fission detector, the size of the fission pulses varies from zero to a maximum value, only a fraction of the fissions occurring in the material can be observed. For absolute measurements of flux or cross section, it is necessary to correct for the finite thickness of the foil; i.e., it is necessary to determine the detection efficiency, defined as the number of observed pulses divided by the number of fissions. For a plane foil of fissionable material, arranged so that no fission fragment can escape from the counting volume without producing a detectable pulse, the detection efficiency is given by

$$F(B) = 1 - \frac{t}{2[R_0 - R(B)]} \tag{2}$$

where t is the thickness of the foil, R_0 is the range of the fission particle in the fissionable material, and $R(B)$ is the range of a fission particle of energy equal to the bias energy B. In deriving this relation (see appendix, Sec. 6), it is assumed all fission fragments have the same range R_0 and that the thickness t of the foil is $t \leqslant [R_0 - R(B)]$. In Fig. 9.1 a calculated bias curve is compared with experimental data. At high bias, the experimental points deviate considerably from the curve. This is to be expected in view of the assumptions made in the calculation. In the case of a cylindrical fission chamber with fissionable material on the inside of the outer electrode, a "wall correction" has to be applied in addition. For an infinitely thin layer of fissionable material, the detection efficiency, which takes into account particles striking the cylindrical wall, is given by

$$F(B) = 1 - \frac{r(B)}{4b} \tag{3}$$

where b is the radius of the chamber and $r(B)$ is that portion of the range of the particle which must be spent in the sensitive volume of the chamber in order to produce a pulse equal to the bias energy B. It is assumed that $r(B)$ is very small compared with b. The necessary data for computing the thickness and the wall corrections are found in the appendix, Sec. 10, which gives stopping power and range-energy relations for fission particles. If both corrections are small, the final expression for the detection efficiency is the product of Eqs. 2 and 3.

Fig. 9.1—Bias curve of an ion-pulse chamber carrying a thin fission foil on a plane electrode. The curve is calculated according to Eq. 3. Crosses represent measurements obtained by using a foil of appropriate thickness.

9.2 Parallel-plate Fission Chamber. A chamber suitable for the absolute measurement of the number of fissions is shown in Fig. 9.2. It is operated at a pressure of 1.5 atm of argon or nitrogen with a collecting voltage of −300 volts at the electrode that carries the foil. The largest amount of Pu^{239} that has been used was 1.2 mg deposited on a circle of 4 cm diameter (95 μg/sq cm). With pure argon, the rise time of pulses was of the order of 1 μsec. The amplifier had a resolving time of 0.1 μsec. This arrangement reduces very effectively the possibility that α particles may pile up to the size of a fission pulse. No such pulse was observed over a period of weeks. Fig. 9.3 shows a bias curve obtained with a 0.434-mg foil of plutonium irradiated with slow neutrons. It shows clearly a practically horizontal plateau over a considerable bias range.

9.3 Small Fission Chamber. A chamber of very small dimensions suitable for quantitative flux measurements is shown in Fig. 9.4. The small dimensions are a particularly desirable feature for measurements of flux in a neutron atmosphere where the introduction of large cavities would change the neutron distribution. The volume of the chamber including the long support is only about 50 cu cm. The chamber is filled with approximately 1 atm of argon. The inner electrode

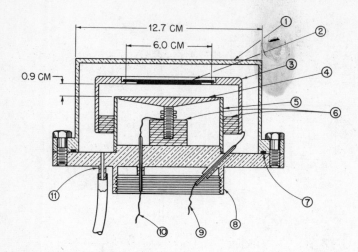

Fig. 9.2—Parallel-plate-type fission chamber for absolute measurements of fission rates. 1, gastight cover. 2, mounting position of sample. 3, high-voltage electrode. 4, collecting electrode. 5, guard electrode. 6, polystyrene insulator. 7, gasket. 8, collar for connection with preamplifier. 9, high-voltage lead. 10, lead to preamplifier. 11, gas inlet.

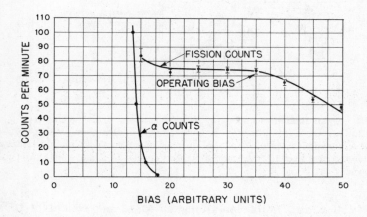

Fig. 9.3—Fission bias curve taken with chamber shown in Fig. 9.2.

serves as both the high-voltage electrode and the collecting electrode; the outer electrode is grounded. The inner electrode is coupled through a small capacitance to the input of the amplifier as shown schematically in Fig. 9.4. No spurious pulses comparable in size to fission pulses were detected when the collecting voltage was kept

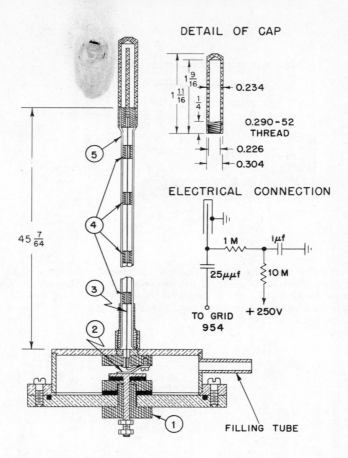

DETAIL OF CAP

ELECTRICAL CONNECTION

Fig. 9.4—Small fission chamber. 1, lucite insulator. 2, contact spring. 3, lead to collecting electrode (No. 28 wire). 4, lucite guides. 5, aluminum shield (0.028-in. wall thickness) forming outer electrode. The inset diagram shows the electrical connections for the case in which the inner electrode serves as a high-voltage and collecting electrode.

below 250 volts. Foils containing up to 10 mg/sq cm of U^{235} were used. The material was deposited on a 1-mil platinum foil which was then rolled into a cylinder and slipped into the chamber. The total amount of material in this case was 60 mg of U_3O_8.

9.4 _Flat Fission Chamber of High Counting Yield._ A chamber for very large amounts of material confined to a comparatively small volume is shown in Fig. 9.5. It was used with 750 mg of U_3O_8 on each plate (63 per cent U^{235} and 37 per cent U^{238}). The chamber was oper-ated at pressures between 1.7 and 3.4 atm of argon with a collecting

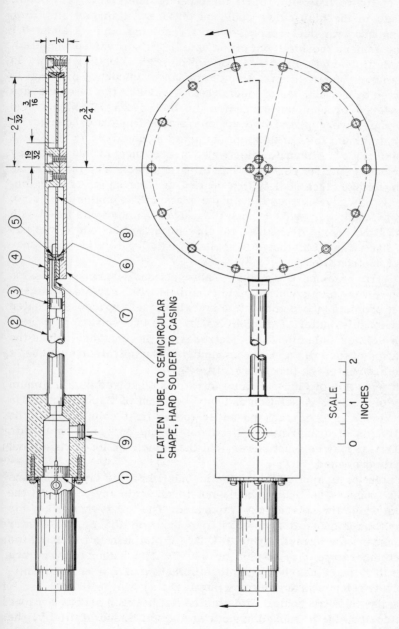

FLATTEN TUBE TO SEMICIRCULAR
SHAPE, HARD SOLDER TO CASING

SCALE

0 1 2

INCHES

Fig. 9.5 — Flat fission chamber of high counting yield. 1, metal-glass seal. 2, $\frac{3}{8}$-in. steel tubing $\frac{1}{32}$-in. wall. 3, lucite support. 4, brass cover plate. 5 and 6, lucite rings. 7, brass bottom plate. 8, support for foils. 9, gas inlet.

voltage of 100 to 200 volts. Since the layer of material is very thick, no plateau in the bias curve could be obtained. Using an amplifier with a square transient response and a resolving time of about 0.1 μsec, no serious trouble from piling up of α pulses was encountered.

9.5 Multiple-plate Fission Chamber of High Counting Yield. In this chamber, shown in Fig. 9.6, a very large amount of material is distributed over a number of electrodes. Twelve of the 14 electrodes were covered with enriched uranium on both sides. The front and bottom plates were plated only on one side. The plates consist of 0.8-mil aluminum foils of 20.5 cm diameter mounted on $\frac{1}{16}$-in.-thick aluminum rings. Alternate electrodes are connected, so that they form two sets, one set serving as a collecting electrode, the other as the high-voltage electrode. With a coating of 1 mg/sq cm of uranium, a total of 7.74 g was deposited on the plates. The material was not highly enriched; only 0.89 g was U^{235}. The chamber was filled with argon at atmospheric pressure. No plateau in the bias curve was obtained. The chamber is therefore suitable only for relative measurements of neutron flux.

9.6 Spiral Fission Chamber. This section describes a fission detector of very high counting yield combined with very small dimensions. It consists of two concentric spirals closely spaced and coated with fissionable material on both sides. The two spirals represent the high-voltage and collecting electrodes of the chamber. Since the preparation of the foils and the assembly of the spirals are unique, a detailed account of the procedure will be given.

(a) Preparation of Foils. Uranyl nitrate is dissolved in a minimum quantity of alcohol. A solution of 1 or 2 per cent of Zapon lacquer in Zapon thinner is prepared and added to the first solution until the concentration of uranyl nitrate is about 50 mg/cu cm. The nitrate concentration may be much lower, but the value mentioned should not be greatly exceeded.

This solution is applied to an aluminum foil in a thin layer by means of a soft brush. The brush should not touch again any portion of the foil from which the solvent has evaporated. The foil is then baked for three or four minutes at about 550°C to burn off the Zapon lacquer and to convert the uranyl nitrate to U_3O_8. If platinum foil is used, the baking temperature may be 800 or 900°C. The higher temperature will result in more nearly complete elimination of Zapon and quantitative conversion of uranyl nitrate into U_3O_8.

When the foil has cooled, it is rolled flat between sheets of paper and the coated side is rubbed smooth with a soft tissue. Initially, the coated surface will exert considerable frictional drag on the tissue

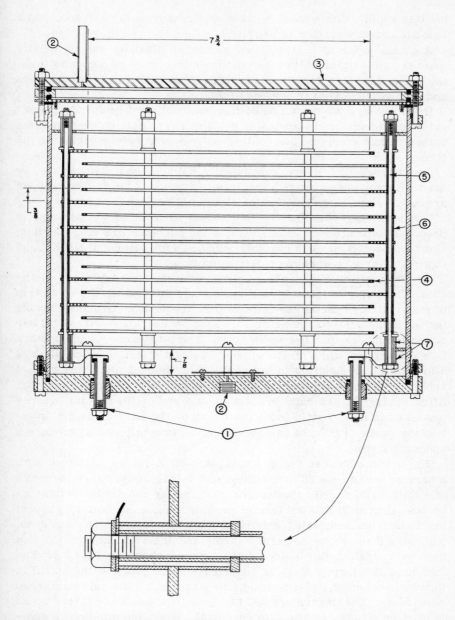

Fig. 9.6—Multiple-plate fission chamber. 1, lead through insulators (lucite). 2, gas inlet. 3, heavy second top plate to be removed after filling of chamber. 4, aluminum rings supporting foils. 5, supporting rod and lead. 6, metal spacer. 7, lucite spacers.

but this rapidly diminishes, without apparent removal of oxide, and a smooth lustrous surface is produced.

A single layer of U_3O_8 applied by this method is, and apparently must be, quite thin. However, the procedure may be repeated until the desired surface density is reached. The coating is very tenacious and will withstand sharp bending of the foil.

If the foil is to be coated on both sides, as it must be for the preparation of spirals, it is advisable to paint alternately on the two sides rather than to complete the coating on one side before beginning the other.

Small areas of foil are conveniently painted, on a flat surface, by hand. Larger areas can be more easily handled if the foil is wrapped around an aluminum drum, which is rotated against the brush.

The aluminum foil that has been used in most of the spirals, is prepared for coating by lightly etching the surfaces in a dilute sodium hydroxide solution. It is carefully cleaned with water and alcohol and thoroughly dried before the painting is begun.

(b) Preparation of Spirals. Spirals have been wound by two methods. The first, illustrated in Figs. 9.7 and 9.8, makes use of a strip of material for spacing the foils as they are wound. Ordinary sewing thread of the desired diameter is wound on a straight stiff metal bar somewhat longer than one of the foils. The turns are wound together tightly until the width of the winding is slightly less than the width of a foil. A dilute solution of Amphenol 912 Cement and thinner or of rubber cement and benzene (1 to 10) is then painted on the threads. After drying, the threads are cut at one end of the bar and are removed from it as a strip twice the length of the bar. In either solution the concentration of cement should be as small as will produce a cohesive strip.

The winding form in Fig. 9.7 is a piece of ¼-in. metal tubing with a narrow smooth-edged longitudinal slot a little deeper than the width of a foil. A flat-faced cylinder 1 in. in diameter and drilled with a ¼-in. hole is pushed into the tube to provide a guide surface to prevent the foils from wandering axially as they are wound. The foil ends, with wire leads soldered across them, are inserted into the slot and bent over against the inside of the tube as shown in Fig. 9.8. The middle of the thread strip is inserted into the slot and the spiral is formed by winding, under tension, half a turn at a time, foil and thread alternately. The fingers are used to smooth the foil and thread so as to produce a tight, evenly spaced spiral. When the winding is completed, narrow strips of an adhesive tape may be wound around the spiral to hold it together temporarily.

Final stages in making a spiral consist in sealing the ends in supporting and insulating material and removing the threads. By exerting

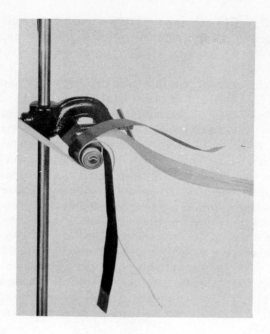

Fig. 9.7 — First method of winding spirals for spiral chamber.

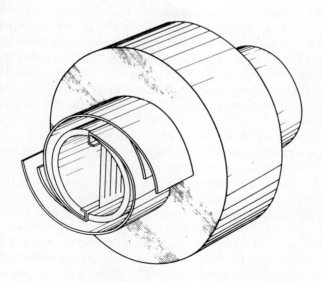

Fig. 9.8 — Fastening of ends of spirals.

force on the guide cylinder, the spiral is pushed partly off the mandrel and about a third of the threads are pulled, one at a time, from the end of the spiral. Wrinkled edges of the foils may be straightened with a scriber.

Sulfur or ordinary red sealing wax provides satisfactory support and insulation for the ends of the spiral. If sulfur is used, the lead wires should be platinum or another metal that does not form a conducting sulfide. Otherwise flakes of sulfide may fall from the wires and short the foils. Ordinary flowers of sulfur does not seem to insulate the foils satisfactorily. Better insulating and mechanical properties are obtained by using a mixture of three parts by weight flowers of sulfur and one part of finely powdered aluminum oxide.

A small quantity of this mixture is melted to the viscous stage on a pyrex plate or other shallow flat-bottomed vessel and is stirred to keep the aluminum oxide in suspension. The exposed end of the spiral, still on the mandrel, is carefully lowered into the molten mixture and gently rotated to cover the entire end of the spiral. Unless the temperature is carefully adjusted, sulfur in its fluid phase will rise to a considerable height between the foils. The central hole in the spiral must be reopened if sulfur has covered it. A heated wire may be used in removing sulfur.

If sealing wax is used for insulation, care is necessary in sealing the second end of the spiral to avoid softening the wax at the other end.

Temporary support for the sealed end is provided by a narrow strip of adhesive tape around the spiral at this end. The tape previously applied is then gently removed and the remaining threads are pulled from the open end of the spiral as before. Tape should be reapplied to keep the outside ends of the foils in place. The wire leads are now bent back on themselves and are pulled through to the completed end of the spiral so that they will not interfere with the sealing of the remaining end.

A set of foils used in one of these spirals is shown in Fig. 9.9. One of the large spirals is ready for dipping while the other is completed and ready for installation in its chamber.

Should the spiral be damaged after completion, the foils may be easily salvaged. Sulfur-insulated spirals may be taken apart by pulling the two foil ends. Those insulated with sealing wax are placed in acetone or alcohol until the foils may be easily pulled apart. All remaining wax is then removed with clean solvent. After all visible traces of insulating material have been removed, the foils should be baked for a few minutes at about 500°C. They may then be smoothed and straightened by placing them between sheets of paper on a flat surface and drawing a smooth cylinder along the foils.

Fig. 9.9—Completed spirals.

A second method of winding spirals uses only two or three threads in the winding process and these remain in the spiral, serving both to support and insulate the foils. This method is particularly adapted to the winding of very small spirals but may also be used in preparing the larger ones.

The winding mandrel consists of two lengths of $\frac{1}{16}$-in. steel rods each milled to a semicircular cross section for about an inch of its length. These are inserted into the bearings of the apparatus shown in Fig. 9.10 so that the milled sections overlap. Threads that have been previously soaked in dilute Amphenol cement and dried are inserted between these sections. Their spacing is determined by the grooved rods in the foreground and background of Fig. 9.10. The ends of the foils are inserted between and on opposite sides of the threads for a little less than $\frac{1}{16}$ in. of their length. They are carefully aligned and the small cylinders are pushed onto the split section to serve as clamps and as guides for the foils. The free ends of the foils are then placed in the clamps shown at the top and bottom of Fig. 9.10.

Tension of the foils and threads is provided by weights and must be adjusted to the foil and thread that are used. Too much tension causes the foils to be creased and the threads to wander. Too little tension produces a loose spiral, which will come apart when it is removed from the machine.

In the case illustrated one lead is soldered to the inside end of one foil and one to the outside end of the other.

Fig. 9.10 — Second method of winding spirals for spiral chamber.

After the alignment has been completed, the spiral is wound by turning the shaft shown in Fig. 9.10. When about 1 in. of foil remains unwound, the top clamp is loosened and a strip of 0.001-in. Amphenol polystyrene tape slightly wider than the foils and about 3 in. long is cemented to the last ¼ in. of this foil. Tension on the foil is maintained manually, and winding is continued until the bottom clamp must be disconnected. The threads will guide the bottom foil for the last half-turn or so. When the end of the top foil has reached the spiral, a sharp razor blade is used to cut the top threads just beyond the end of the top foil. After a further half-turn the other threads are similarly cut. With the guide cylinders pushed back, several layers of the Amphenol tape are applied and the end is fastened down with a small drop of Amphenol cement.

The spiral is now completed and is removed from the machine by loosening the set screws that hold the split rods in their bearings and pulling the rods from the spiral. If the spiral is shorted, the trouble will generally be found in the center of the winding. Careful probing in the $\frac{1}{16}$-in. central hole will usually remove the distortion that shorts the foils. Small spirals produced by the above technique are shown in Fig. 9.11.

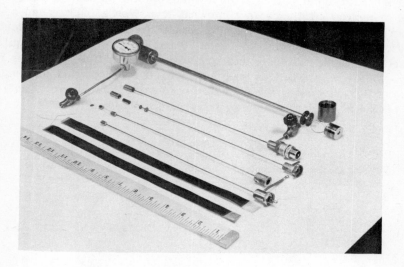

Fig. 9.11 — Three spiral chambers of different sizes ready for assembly. In the foreground are two coated foils.

The spirals are mounted in a suitable small container. A completed chamber is connected to the filling system at the valve provided and is evacuated. The entire chamber is baked until evolution of vapors is negligible. The temperature of the spiral end of the chamber will be limited, of course, by the melting or softening temperatures of the insulating material of the spiral or by the solder used in sealing the chamber. Since the spacing of the two foils is quite small (0.02 in.), it is necessary to operate the chambers at rather high pressure, from 5 to 10 atm of argon for the larger type, and from 10 to 14 atm for the smaller type. For the same reason the collecting voltage is quite low; 135 volts proved to be satisfactory for both types regardless of foil spacing.

The capacity of the spiral chambers is as high as 500 $\mu\mu$f. They can be operated either by grounding one foil and using the other as high-voltage and collecting electrode, or by applying the high voltage to one spiral and using the other as collecting electrode. In the first case, the collecting voltage is applied through a 0.25-megohm resistor and the input of the amplifier is coupled through a condenser of 100 to 500 $\mu\mu$f. In the second case, the leak resistor should be about 0.1 megohm. Because of the large amount of material used in these detectors, the counting bias has to be set at a comparatively high value, in order to avoid pulses from a piling up of α pulses. Consequently the detection efficiency is somewhat low. For a background of not more than one to two counts per minute due to pile-up, the detection efficiency was found to be between 80 and 90 per cent. The amplifier used with these chambers had a resolving time of 1.5 μsec. The rise time of the pulses is less than 0.2 μsec. If not more than 0.25 mg/sq cm of U_3O_8 are used, the bias curves show a flat plateau. Table 9.1 gives a list of constructions that were actually used.

Table 9.1

Foil spacing, mils	Diameter, in.	Length, in.	Useful area, sq cm	Max. deposit, mg U
20	1	1	200	240
20	1	1	360	550
7	3/8	0.3	22	35

9.7 **Integrating Fission Chambers.** Figure 9.12 shows an integrating chamber used for relative flux measurements in very dense slow-neutron atmospheres. The ionization current can be measured directly with a galvanometer. The chamber is constructed in such a way that the ionization current is produced predominantly by fission fragments and only to a small extent by γ rays or electrons. One hundred and eighty-four milligrams of U^{235} (345 mg of 63.1 per cent enriched U_3O_8) are deposited in the form of nitrate on both sides of the 14 electrodes with the exception of the end plates, which are coated only on one side. The plate spacing is $25/32$ in. Alternate plates are connected to the collecting and to the high-voltage leads. It was found that residual ionization due to the β activity of the chamber material, produced by previous neutron bombardment, could be greatly reduced by using ordinary cold-rolled iron for the container and parts of the internal structure. The chamber is filled to a pressure of 1 atm of argon and operated with voltages up to 1,800 volts. With the maximum voltage, a linear relation between ionization current and neutron flux was found for currents up to 21 μamp.

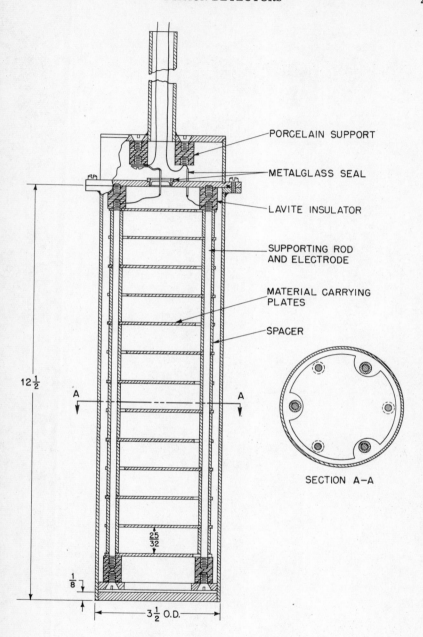

Fig. 9.12 — Integrating fission chamber.

APPENDIX

1. Range-Energy Relations and Stopping Power. Figures 1, 2, and 3 show the range-energy relations for α particles, protons, and deuterons in air at normal temperature and pressure (760 mm Hg, 15°C) according to Livingston and Bethe.* These curves were obtained by fitting theoretical expressions to experimental data. In order to obtain the range-energy relation for deuterons, note that a deuteron of energy 2E has twice the range of a proton of energy E.

Figure 4 shows the range-energy relation for protons in argon computed according to Bethé's methods. The results were fitted to experimental values. In addition to the range-energy relation, Fig. 4 shows the stopping cross section σ as a function of energy. This quantity is directly connected with the specific energy loss $-dE/dx$ by

$$\sigma = -\frac{1}{n}\frac{dE}{dx}$$

where n is the number of atoms per cubic centimeter (at N.T.P., $n = 2.548 \times 10^{19}$). The third curve in Fig. 4 marked $\bar{x}$ gives the distance of the center of gravity of ionization of a track of energy E from the point of origin of the particle measured along its path

$$\bar{x}(E_0) = R(E_0) - \frac{1}{E_0}\int_0^{E_0} R(E)\ dE = \frac{1}{E_0}\int_0^R \frac{-dE}{dx}\ x\ dx \qquad (1)$$

Figure 5 shows the same three quantities for xenon.

Figures 6 and 7 show the range-energy relations of protons in paraffin ($C_n H_{2n+2}$) and glycerol tristearate. The curves are based upon calculated values of the stopping number B in C, O, and H. The stopping number B is related to the energy loss $-dE/dx$ by the equation

$$-\frac{dE}{dx} = \frac{4\pi\,e^4 z^2}{mv^2}\,nB \qquad (2)$$

*Livingston and Bethe, Revs. Modern Phys. 9: 281 (1937).

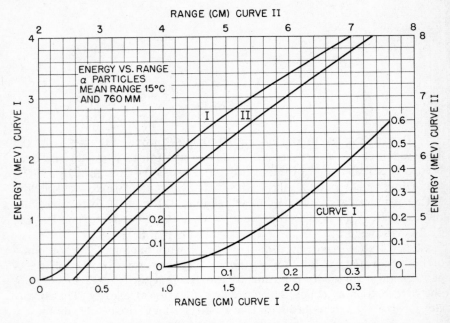

Fig. 1 — Range-energy relation for α particles (Livingston and Bethe).

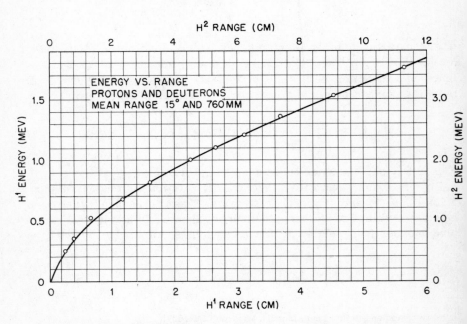

Fig. 2 — Range-energy relation for protons and deuterons (Livingston and Bethe).

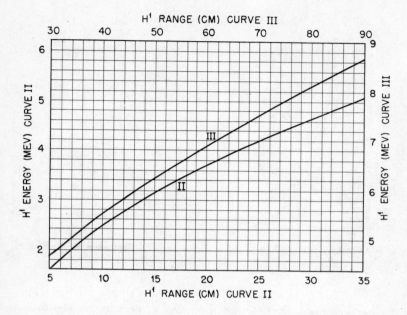

Fig. 3 — Range-energy relation for protons (Livingston and Bethe).

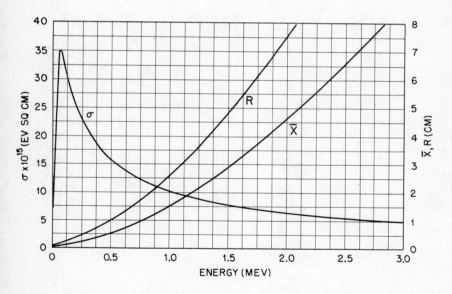

Fig. 4 — Range, stopping cross section, and center of ionization for protons in argon (760 mm Hg; 15°C).

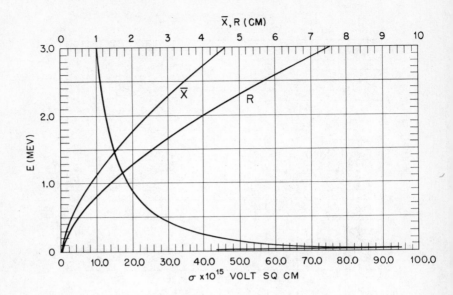

Fig. 5—Range, stopping cross section, and center of ionization for protons in xenon (760 mm Hg; 15°C).

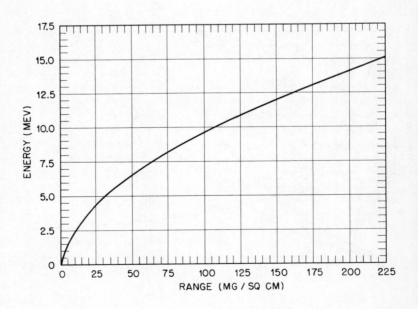

Fig. 6—Range-energy relation for protons in paraffin.

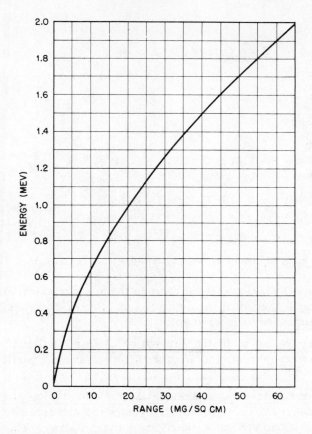

Fig. 7—Range-energy relation for protons in glycerol tristearate.

where m is the electron mass, e is the electron charge, ze is the charge of the incident particle, and v is its velocity. The expressions used for the computation of these curves are:

Carbon:

$B_C = 9.4406 \log (E/0.0094704) - 2.2652\ C_K(1/\eta_L)$
$\quad + 4.3479 \log (E/0.22356) - 1.0497\ C_K(1/\eta_K)$ for $E \geq 0.8$

$B_C = 9.4406 \log (E/0.0094704) - 2.2652\ C_K(1/\eta_L)$
$\quad + 1.0497\ B_K(\eta_K)$ for $0.03 \leq E \leq 0.8$

$B_C = 2.2652\ B_K(\eta_L) + 1.0497\ B_K(\eta_K)$ for $E \leq 0.03$

where $\eta_K = E/0.811520$ and $\eta_L = E/0.034378$

Hydrogen:

$$B_H = 2.30259 \log E - 0.55248 \, C_K(1/\eta) + 4.800 \qquad \text{for } E \geq 0.03$$

$$B_H = (E/1.81) \, B_K(\eta) \qquad \text{for } E \leq 0.03$$

where $\eta = E/0.029863$

Oxygen:

$$B_O = 18.421 \log E - 3.4199 \, C_K(1/\eta_L) - C_K(1/\eta_K) \\ + 24.741 \qquad \text{for } E \geq 1.5$$

$$B_O = 14.253 \log E - 3.4199 \, C_K(1/\eta_L) + B_K(\eta_K) \\ + 22.496 \qquad \text{for } 0.09 \leq E \leq 1.5$$

$$B_O = 3.4199 \, B_K(\eta_L) + B_K(\eta_K) \qquad \text{for } E \leq 0.09$$

where $\eta_K = E/1.4809$ and $\eta_L = E/0.09036$

The functions $C_K(1/\eta)$ and $B_K(\eta)$ used in these expressions are represented in Fig. 8 according to Livingston and Bethe. The energies have to be taken in million electron volts.

2. <u>Energy W_0 Spent in the Formation of One Ion Pair.</u>   Table 1 gives the various values of W_0 for different gases, particles, and energies.

3. <u>Range of Electrons in Aluminum; Specific Ionization of Electrons in Air.</u>   The curves in Figs. 9a and 9b show the extrapolated range of electrons in aluminum as a function of their energy. The curve in Fig. 9c shows their specific ionization in ion pairs per centimeter in air for normal temperature and pressure.

4. <u>Scattering Cross Sections of Protons and Deuterons for Neutrons.</u> Figures 10 and 11 show the scattering cross sections of protons and deuterons (at rest) vs. the energy of the impinging neutrons. The proton curve is the plot of a theoretical expression that fits the experimental data very well. The deuteron curve is purely experimental.

5. <u>Coefficients of Attenuation of γ Rays in Al, Cu, Sn, and Pb.</u> Figure 12 shows a plot of the coefficients of attenuation τ of γ rays for Al, Cu, Sn, and Pb vs. the energy of the quantum, according to Heitler.* In the case of lead, the three components of τ (i.e., the photoelectric effect, Compton effect, and pair-production coefficient)

---

*W. Heitler, "Quantum Theory of Radiation," 2d ed., Oxford University Press, Oxford, 1944.

Table 1 — Values of W_0

Gas	W_0, ev	Particle	Energy, mev	Reference
Air	32.0	Electrons	0.3	
Air	36.0	Protons	2.5-7.5	
Air	35.1	α particles	7.8	L. H. Gray, Proc. Cambridge Phil.
Air	35.6	α particles	5.3	Soc., 40: 72 (1944)
H_2	36.0	α particles	5.3	
He	31.0	α particles	5.3	
CO	34.7	α particles	5.3	
CO_2	34.6	α particles	5.3	K. Schmieder, Ann. Physik, 35: 445
C_2H_4	27.6	α particles	5.3	(1939)
C_2H_4	28.2	α particles	5.3	
C_2H_2	27.6	α particles	5.3	
Ne	27.8	α particles	5.3	K. Schmieder, Ann. Physik, 35: 445
A	24.9	α particles	5.3	(1939)
A	26.9	Electrons	0.0174	D. B. Nicodemus, Thesis, Stanford University, 1946
Kr	23.0	α particles	5.3	K. Schmieder, Ann. Physik, 35: 445 (1939)
Xe	21.4	α particles	1.3	R. W. Gurney, Proc. Roy. Soc. London, A107: 332 (1925)

energy $E \gg B$ in the detector is counted. The observed number of counts C divided by the true number of disintegration C_0 is the detection efficiency F at the bias B. The number of counted particles from a layer between x and x + dx (see Fig. 13) is given by

$$dC = \int_0^{\theta_0} 2\pi \sin \theta \; d\theta \; dx$$

where θ_0 is that angle at which the particle, upon emerging from the foil, has just enough energy to be counted. Let the range at this energy be R(B), and the original range R_0, both measured in the material of the foil. Then

$$R(B) = R_0 - \frac{x}{\cos \theta_0}$$

are shown. If σ is the total cross section per atom and n is the number of atoms per cubic centimeter, then τ is defined as $\tau = n\sigma$.

6. Thickness Correction for Plane Foils. Suppose particles of uniform range are emitted isotropically from a material layer of thickness t, one particle being emitted per disintegration. The recording device shall be biased so every particle losing an amount of

and the total number of counts is

$$C = 2\pi \int_0^t dx \cdot \int_0^{\theta_0} \sin\theta \; d\theta = 2\pi t \left\{ 1 - \frac{t}{2[R_0 - R(B)]} \right\}$$

Since $C_0 = 4\pi t$, it follows that

$$F(B) = \frac{1}{2} \left\{ 1 - \frac{t}{2[R_0 - R(B)]} \right\} \tag{3}$$

The relation is, of course, valid only if $t \leq [R_0 - R(B)]$. It is assumed that the pulse size is independent of the direction of the particle. Since θ_0 is taken to be rather large, the effect of electron collection may be neglected if the foil is on the negative electrode.

For low-biased boron detectors, the detection efficiency will be the sum of the efficiencies for α particles and lithium recoils as shown in Chap. 8. For fission detectors, since two fragments are emitted per disintegration, the detection efficiency is twice that given by formula (3), as stated in Sec. 9.1. For reactions giving rise to single particles of uniform energy and for thick layers, when $t \geq [R_0 - R(B)]$, F is given by

$$F(B) = \frac{R_0 - R(B)}{4t} \tag{4}$$

7. Range of Lithium Recoils and Atomic Stopping Power of Boron. An approximate range-energy relation for Li[7] has been constructed from the photometric traces of cloud-chamber tracks from the $B(n,\alpha)$ disintegrations of Bower, Bretscher, and Gilbert. Within the considerable uncertainty it was found that the same energy-range relation holds for Li[7] as for slow α particles. The atomic stopping power of boron relative to air for very slow α particles has been estimated by interpolation to be about 0.8.

8. Detection Efficiency of Cylindrical Detector with Radiator. If a foil containing the emitting substance is placed on the inside of the wall of a cylindrical detector of radius b, the detection efficiency is reduced because some of the particles will leave the counting volume by striking the cylindrical wall surface. This effect is assumed to be small. This assumption requires that $r(B) \gg b$, where $r(B)$ is that part of the initial range in the gas of the detector required to produce a measurable pulse. For the computation of the detection efficiency, the same assumptions shall be made as in the appendix, Sec. 6, and it shall, moreover, be assumed that the active layer is infinitely thin.

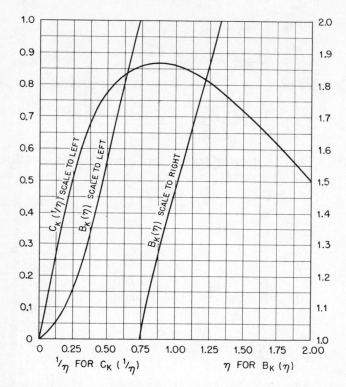

Fig. 8 — The functions $B_K(\eta)$ and $C_K(1/\eta)$ for the calculation of stopping numbers. [M. S. Livingston and H. A. Bethe, Revs. Modern Phys., 9: 245 (1937).]

Referring to Fig. 14, it can be seen that the detection efficiency is given by the ratio of the area of a sphere of radius r(B) inside the cylinder to its total area $4\pi r^2(B)$. Introducing a polar coordinate system with its origin in the cylinder, the polar axis along the radius, and the plane $\phi = 0$ perpendicular to the axis of the cylinder, the difference f between the surface of the half sphere and the surface inside the cylinder is given by

$$f = \iint r^2 \sin \theta \; d\theta \; d\phi$$

The boundary curve of the surface is given by the equations of the sphere and the cylinder

$$r = r(B)$$

$$r^2 \sin^2 \theta \cos^2 \phi + r^2 \cos^2 \theta - 2rb \cos \theta = 0$$

If $\cos \theta = \mu$, then

$$f = r^2(B) \int_0^{2\pi} d\phi \int_0^{\mu_1} d\mu$$

where μ_1 is given by the equation of the boundary curve

$$\mu_1 = \frac{1 - \sqrt{1 - \{[r(B)/b] \sin \phi \cos \phi\}^2}}{\sin \phi [r(B)/b]}$$

Expanding μ_1 and neglecting higher than linear terms in $r(B)/b$ gives

$$f = \frac{\pi}{2} \frac{r^3(B)}{b}$$

and

$$F(B) = \frac{1}{2} \left[1 - \frac{r(B)}{4b} \right] \qquad (5)$$

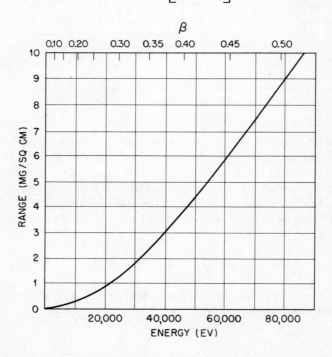

Fig. 9a—Range of slow electrons in aluminum. (Rasetti, "Elements of Nuclear Physics.")

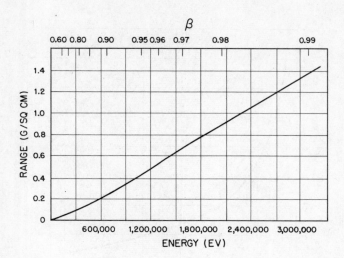

Fig. 9b — Range of fast electrons in aluminum. (Rasetti, "Elements of Nuclear Physics.")

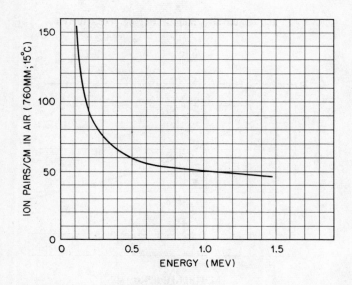

Fig. 9c — Specific ionization of fast electrons in air. (Rutherford, Chadwick, and Ellis, "Radiation from Radioactive Substances.")

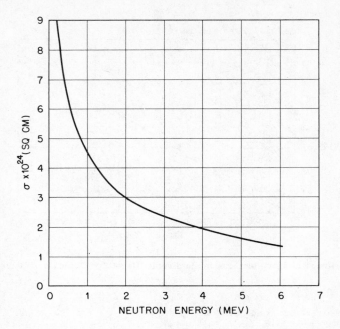

Fig. 10 — Neutron-proton scattering cross section.

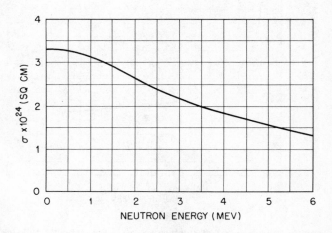

Fig. 11 — Neutron-deuteron scattering cross section.

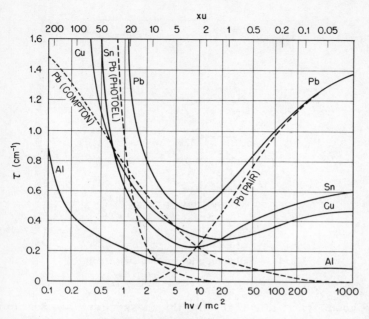

Fig. 12 — Attenuation coefficient for γ rays in Pb, Sn, Cu, and Al as a function of frequency (Heitler, "The Quantum Theory of Radiation"). The dotted curves show the three components of τ for lead.

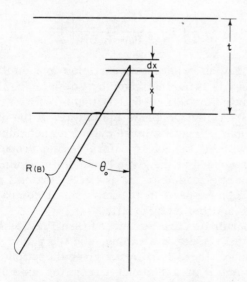

Fig. 13 — Thickness correction for plane foil.

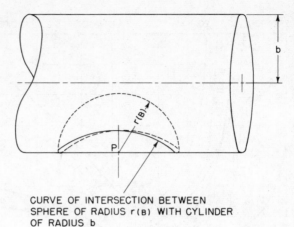

CURVE OF INTERSECTION BETWEEN
SPHERE OF RADIUS r(B) WITH CYLINDER
OF RADIUS b

Fig. 14 — Wall correction for cylindrical foil.

If the geometrical effect and the thickness effect (see Sec. 6) are both small, i.e., if the respective correction factors are close to 1, the total correction factor is the product of the two individual correction factors, and the detection efficiency is given by the equation

$$F(B)_{total} = \frac{1}{2}\left\{1 - \frac{t}{2[R_0 - R(B)]}\right\}\left[1 - \frac{r(B)}{4b}\right] \tag{5a}$$

In the case of fissions, where two particles are emitted, the total detection efficiency is twice that given by Eq. 5a.

9. Wall Correction for Cylindrical Detector with Very Small Inner Electrode When Particles Originate in the Gas. If the disintegrations take place in the gas filling of a large cylindrical chamber of radius b, some particles will hit the walls before having produced sufficient ionization to be recorded at the given bias. It is assumed that all the disintegration energy goes into one particle, that all particles have the same range R_0 measured in the gas (small compared to b), and that particles are emitted isotropically.

If cartesian coordinates are introduced (see Fig. 15) with the origin at the point P, the z axis on a radius, and the y axis parallel to the axis of the cylinder, there is, for any given direction of emission of the particle, a point P at a distance η from the axis 0 such that the particle loses an energy B equal to the bias energy before striking

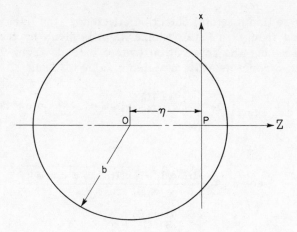

Fig. 15—Wall correction for cylindrical chamber when ionizing particles originate in gas.

the wall. For particles emitted in the direction given by the polar angles θ and ϕ, the detection efficiency is

$$dF = \left[\frac{\eta(\theta,\phi)}{b}\right]^2 \frac{\sin\theta \; d\theta \; d\phi}{4\pi}$$

The equation for the cylindrical wall is

$$(r\cos\theta + \eta)^2 + (r\sin\theta\cos\phi)^2 = b^2 \qquad\qquad (6)$$

and

$$\eta^2 \approx b^2\left[1 - \frac{2r}{b}\cos\theta\right]$$

if terms of higher order in (r/b) are neglected. This determines η for every given r, θ, and ϕ. Let $r(B)$ be that portion of the initial range that has to be within the sensitive volume in order to produce a pulse of size equal to the bias energy

$$r(B) = R_0 - R(E_0 - B)$$

where R_0 is the original range of the particles, E_0 is the original energy, and B is the bias energy.

In order to find the total detection efficiency, the integration has to be extended from 0 to $\theta_m(\phi)$, where $\theta_m(\phi)$ is given by the relation in Eq. 6 with $\eta = b$. The integration over ϕ extends from 0 to 2π. For $\theta_m \leq \theta \leq \pi$, η remains at its maximum value b. Thus

$$F(B) = \frac{1}{4\pi} \int_0^{2\pi} d\phi \left\{ \int_0^{\theta_m} \left(\frac{\eta^2}{b^2}\right) \sin\theta \; d\theta + \int_{\theta_m}^{\pi} \sin\theta \; d\theta \right.$$

with

$$\cos\theta_m = \frac{-b \pm \sqrt{b^2 - [r(B)\sin\phi\cos\phi]^2}}{r(B)\sin^2\phi}$$

$$\approx -\frac{1}{2} \frac{r(B)}{b} \cos^2\phi$$

Within the above approximation, F becomes

$$F = 1 - \frac{r(B)}{2b} \tag{7}$$

10. Range-Energy Relation for Fission Fragments; Stopping Power of Various Materials for Fission Fragments. The mean range of fission fragments in various materials computed from the measurements of Bohr, Boeggild, Brostroem, and Lauritsen is shown in Fig. 16. The two curves represent averages for the two groups of fission fragments.

It was found that approximately all materials have the same stopping power for fission fragments as for α particles of 4.5 mev. The data for air were taken from the above reference. Values of the mean range of fission fragments and the stopping power of various materials for fission fragments are given in Table 2. The values for the ranges are not considered to be very accurate except for air.

11. Resolution and Piling Up of Pulses. In the following discussion of the resolution of pulses, two cases will be treated.

In the first case, it is assumed that every pulse counted paralyzes the detection equipment for a time τ, which is large compared with the duration of the pulse. The dead time τ shall be independent of any other pulse occurring during this time. Such a situation arises, for instance, with a Geiger-Mueller counter or a thyratron triggered by a very short pulse. The probability that n − 1 additional pulses occur within the time τ after the occurrence of a pulse is given by Poisson's formula

$$P(n-1) = \frac{(\tau n_0)^{n-1}}{(n-1)!} e^{-\tau n_0} \tag{8}$$

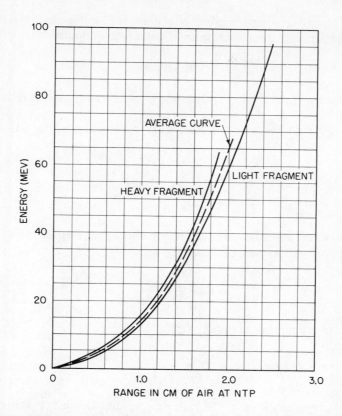

Fig. 16—Range-energy relation for fission fragments. [Bohr, Boeggild, Brostroem, and Lauritsen, Phys. Rev., 58: 839 (1940); Boeggild, Brostroem, and Lauritsen, Phys. Rev., 59: 275 (1941).]

Table 2—Mean Range of Fission Fragments and Atomic Stopping Power

Material	Mean range of fission fragments, mg/sq cm	Atomic stopping power
Air	2.70	1.00
Al	3.7	1.51
Collodion	2.6	
Cu	5.2	2.40
Ag	6.1	3.08
Au	11.14	3.96
U	12.6 (estimated)	4.2
U_3O_8	10.0 (estimated)	4.2

where n_0 is the average number of pulses per unit time. The number of counts per unit time containing n pulses is given by

$$C(n) = K \cdot P(n - 1)$$

where the constant K is determined by the normalizing condition

$$n_0 = \sum_1^\infty KP(n - 1) \, n = K \sum_1^\infty P(n - 1)(n - 1 + 1) = K(\tau n_0 + 1)$$

Thus

$$C(n) = \frac{n_0}{1 + \tau n_0} \frac{(\tau n_0)^{n - 1}}{(n - 1)!} e^{-\tau n_0} \tag{9}$$

The total counting rate (number of counts per unit time, irrespective of how many pulses are contained in a count) is

$$C_0 = \frac{n_0}{1 + \tau n_0} \tag{10}$$

The relative counting loss is

$$L = \frac{n_0 - C_0}{n_0} = \frac{\tau n_0}{1 + \tau n_0} \tag{11}$$

A very convenient way of determining τ, and therefore the counting loss, consists in comparing the counting rates C_{01} and C_{02} of two sources having pulse rates n_{01} and n_{02} with the counting rate C_{012} of the combined source, which is given by

$$C_{012} = \frac{n_{01} + n_{02}}{1 + \tau(n_{01} + n_{02})} = \frac{C_{01} + C_{02} - 2\tau C_{01}C_{02}}{1 - \tau^2 C_{01}C_{02}} \tag{12}$$

The rate of accidental coincidences G of two recording devices giving pulses of duration τ and having counting rates C_{01} and C_{02} is given by the equation

$$G = \sum_2^\infty C_{12}(n) - \sum_1^\infty C_1(n) - \sum_2^\infty C_2(n)$$

For $(C_{01} + C_{02}) \ll 1$, neglecting higher than linear terms

$$G = 2\tau C_{01} \cdot C_{02} \tag{13}$$

As a second case, consider that the dead time is not a constant, independent of subsequent counts falling within τ, but that the recording instrument records a pulse whenever the voltage of the collecting electrode has been at zero for any arbitrary short time preceding the pulse. Again let n_0 be the pulse rate. The probability that a pulse is followed by a "gap" of duration τ (no further pulse during the time τ) is given by $e^{-\tau n_0}$. Thus the counting rate C_0 (number of recorded counts per unit time) is

$$C_0 = n_0 e^{-\tau n_0} \tag{14}$$

The numbers of single, double, and n-fold counts are, respectively,

$$C(1) = n_0 e^{-2\tau n_0}$$

since a gap of at least τ is required before and after a pulse;

$$C(2) = n_0 e^{-2\tau n_0} (1 - e^{-\tau n_0})$$

requiring that the pulse be followed by one other within the time τ; and

$$C(n) = n_0 e^{-2\tau n_0} (1 - e^{-\tau n_0})^{n-1} \tag{15}$$

For the determination of τ, using the same notations as before, and provided that $n_{01}\tau$ and $n_{02}\tau$ are both small, the following relation holds:

$$\tau = \frac{C_{01} + C_{02} - C_{012}}{2 \, C_{01} C_{02}} \tag{16}$$

The piling up of square pulses of uniform height P and equal width τ will be considered next.

A pulse height nP is produced if n pulses occur within a time τ. The counting rate for pulses of height nP is therefore the counting rate C(n), as given in Eq. 9. It should be kept in mind that the height nP exists only during a time smaller than τ. Consequently, many of the multiple pulses are of very short duration. In practical cases, where the pulses usually have an exponential rise and decay, the formula gives approximate values if τ is taken as equal to the resolving time. For an accurate treatment of practical cases, knowledge of the complete transient response of the detecting equipment is necessary.

12. Numerical Values of the Back-scattering Function Φ for α particles.

1. Relative values of Φ for various materials:

Material	$\Phi_{material}/\Phi_{gold}$
Au	1.00
Pt	0.99
U_3O_8	0.894
SiO_2	0.19
Al	0.23
Be	0.10

2. Values of Φ for gold using α particles of 3.68 cm range (N.T.P.) at various values of $R(B)$ in air; $R(B)$ = the range of an α particle of energy equal to the bias energy B:

$R(B)$, cm	$\Phi \times 10^2$
0	9.7
0.1	9.0
0.2	8.5
0.3	8.0
0.4	7.7
0.5	7.5

3. For the variations of Φ with the range R_0 of the α particles, it can be assumed approximately that

$$\Phi^2(R_0) = \Phi^2(3.68) \cdot \frac{3.68}{R_0(cm)}$$

or that Φ varies approximately inversely with the square root of the range.

INDEX

Gas multiplication, definition, 72
  in argon, 80, 81
  in boron trifluoride, 83
  in gas mixtures, 84-87
  in hydrogen, 78
  in methane, 79
  in nitrogen, 82
Geiger-Mueller counter, for β rays, 115
  for γ rays, 116
  with mica window, 116
Grid chamber, 124

H

Hydrogen recoil chamber (see Chamber)

I

Integrating chamber (see Chamber)
Ionization, 1
  by collision, 72
Ionization current, 20-22
  chamber (see Chamber)
  pulse, 37

M

Mobility, 18

N

Neutron flux, measurement, 156, 178,
    186, 203, 206, 218
  fast neutrons, 156, 162, 165, 174,
    176
  slow neutrons, 186, 206
Neutron spectrometer (see Spectrometer)

P

Parallel plate chamber (see Chamber)
Path, mean free, 6
  of electrons, 15, 18
Power, stopping, 131n, 221
  of boron, 228
  of fission fragments, 236
Proportional counter (see Counter)

Pulsed counter, 117
Pulse, height of, 38, 42
  effect of diffusion on, 53
  piling up of, 236-239
  shape of, 39, 62, 88

R

Range-energy relation, 221-226, 228,
  230, 231, 236
Recombination, 2, 27, 29
  columnar, 15
Recombination constant, 2, 15, 19
Resolution, 236-239
Response, transient, of amplifier, 39
  of detecting equipment, 41
  of ionization chamber, 40-41

S

Spectrometer, neutron, 158, 162, 186
Stopping number, 221

T

Thickness correction, for α-particle
  detectors, 126
  for fission detectors, 205
  for plane foils, 227-228

U

Uranium hexafluoride, 203

V

Velocity, agitation, 1
  of electrons, 15, 18
  transport, 2

W

Wall correction, for cylindrical detectors, 234-235
  for fission detectors, 205
  for gas recoil chambers, 153-154